Santa Clara County Free Library

REFERENCE

5816

GREAT HOT SPRINGS
OF THE WEST

BILL KAYSING

Cover photo: Rogers Hot Springs, northeast of Las Vegas.

PARALIPOMENA

Orthographiæ, Etymologiæ, Prosodiæ: vnà cum

Scholijs

Ad Canones, de Genere Substantiuorũ, de Anomalis,
Præterito et Supinis verborũ, Syntaxi, Carminũ
ratione, et Figuris.

Ex optimis Authoribus, et Gramaticorũ
Coryphæis, collecta et asserta.

In 4: libros distributa.

Studio et industria

Joannis Danesij

Dulcius ex ipso Fonte bibuntur aquæ

Londinij Typis I.L. Impensis Ph: Stephani & Ch: Meredithij Sub
aureo Leone in Cæmeterio Paulino. 1639

CAPRA PRESS TITLES
DEALING WITH WESTERN MAN IN WATER:

HOT TUBS, Leon Elder

FREE BEACHES, Elder/Crawford
(With a Foreword by Dr. Alex Comfort)

GREAT HOT SPRINGS OF THE WEST, Bill Kaysing

GREAT SWIMMING HOLES OF THE WEST, Bill Kaysing (1975)

GREAT HOT SPRINGS OF THE WEST

by

BILL KAYSING

Foreword by Leon Elder

Describing his Journeys to Memorable
Hot Springs in California, Oregon,
Idaho, Nevada, and New Mexico,
with a full Directory of all Those
in the Western United States.

(INCLUDING PROFUSE PHOTOS)

1974

CAPRA PRESS   SANTA BARBARA

Cover Art by Courtlandt Johnson

A larger book would have permitted the inclusion of many of the well-developed hot springs resorts, such as Murrieta, Gilman, Seminole, or Desert Hot Springs. However, with only so many pages for more than a thousand springs, we decided to omit these well-advertised and popular facilities. They are great hot springs in every sense of the word . . . otherwise they would not have attracted so many people for so many years. Thus, those who own or manage hot springs and don't find them included herein should know that they are not being omitted for lack of appeal, just space.

GRATEFUL ACKNOWLEDGMENTS TO: Dave Bohn for the photo of Byron Hot Springs on page 15; Tim Crawford for the photo of Little Caliente on page 18; Santa Barbara Historical Society for the photos on pages 2 and 23; Joel Conway Historical Collection for the photo of the Veronica bottle on page 23; Jim Tyne for the photo of Lava Hot Springs on page 39; the U.S. Department of Interior for photos on pages 10, 11 and 72; to the New Mexico Department of Development for the photo of Ojo Caliente on page 50; Judith Young for graphic research; Patty Yancey for layout; Mackintosh Typography for typesetting; and to the Great Outdoors for providing the subject matter for this book.

Printed in Santa Barbara by Haagen Printing Company.

ISBN 0-912264-89-6

CAPRA PRESS
631 State Street
Santa Barbara, Ca. 93101

TABLE OF CONTENTS

FOREWORD by Leon Elder 7

INTRODUCTION
Why Hot Springs? 9
What is a Hot Spring? 10
Types of Springs 12
Unusual Springs 12
Some Background 13
Hot Springs Equipment 14

THE GREAT AND NEAR-GREAT
CALIFORNIA:
Byron Hot Springs 15
Big Caliente 16
Little Caliente 18
Oh My God Hot Springs 19
Kelly's Hot Springs 20
Grover Hot Springs 20
Brockway 21
Hot Creek 22
Campbell Hot Springs 22
Paraiso Hot Springs 22
Keene Wonder Springs 23

OREGON:
General 24
Vale Hot Springs 25
Summer Lake 26
Ana Hot Springs 27
Capra Springs 28
Belknap Hot Springs 29
Hunter's Lodge 30
Crane Hot Springs 30
Hidaway Hot Springs 31
Lehman Hot Springs 32
Hot Lake 33
Soda Lake 34
Ritter Hot Springs 35
Breitenbush Hot Springs 36
A New One 36

IDAHO:
Clarendon Hot Springs 37
Warswick Hot Springs 38
Lava Hot Springs 39

Russian John Hot Springs 40
Leon's Hot Springs 40
Challis Hot Springs 41
Robinson Bar Ranch 42
Sullivan Hot Springs 44
Riggins Hot Springs 45
Salmon Hot Springs 46

NEVADA:
Spencer Hot Springs 47

NEW MEXICO:
Ojo Caliente 50
Jemez Hot Springs 50
Spence Hot Springs 50

OWN YOUR OWN
Orr's Hot Springs 51
Medical Springs 51

THE DIRECTORY AND MAPS 52
Using the Directory 53
California-Nevada Map 54
California Hot Springs 55
Nevada Hot Springs 60
Oregon Map 66
Oregon Hot Springs 67
Idaho Map 71
Idaho Hot Springs 72
Wyoming Map 78
Wyoming Hot Springs 79
Utah Map 85
Utah Hot Springs 86
Montana Hot Springs 88
Arizona Hot Springs 89
Washington Hot Springs 89
Colorado Hot Springs 90
New Mexico Hot Springs 91
Alaska Map 92
Alaska Hot Springs 93

RATING CHART 95

THANK YOU PAGE 96

in Sculp.

FOREWORD

I'd been working on stone walls all day at Henry Miller's place up on Partington Ridge. At that elevation the summer was hot and unremitting although the coast road, a thousand feet below, was fogged in. In the later afternoon, having finished his daily time of writing, Henry took mercy and suggested we take wine and cheese and soak at the Hot Springs, a few miles down the Big Sur road.

We stopped at Anderson Creek where friends lived in shacks built for the convict labor that had carved the road years before, and picked up a couple of passengers. In those pre-Esalen days, the Hot Springs was a welcome road stop for coast travelers. There was a restaurant, craft shop, a few rustic cabins and those remarkable tubs dug into the cliff below. This was in the early fifties before the invention of franchised motels and pancake houses. The spa was crude enough to be convivial, waitresses played guitars in idle moments. There was no turnstile. Fifty cents gave you a towel and the right to soak as long as you wanted.

It was a bit chilly near the ocean. I followed Henry down the path to the tub house, a redwood shelter with three walls built against the cliff. The fourth side was open—a deck that jutted over the ocean, a hundred feet below. A cement trough ran along the back wall behind a row of bathtubs and one communal bath. You filled your tub by pulling out a whittled plug. Scalding, sulfurous water poured in, then you tempered it with a coldwater hose. This was my first visit to a hot spring.

We laid side by side in adjoining tubs and mused aloud amongst ourselves. Hot steam rose up and twined with the incoming fog. Our ideas vaporized and reformed, hot and cold. Heat worked into my bones. I sat up on the curled edge of the iron tub and found the chill air bracing, like an icy drink on a hot day. In ten minutes or so the chill got to me and I sank back happily into the fuming water. Henry and his cronies, I noticed, had stretched themselves out belly down on the plank tables, dozing or staring at the sea.

Big Sur then was Olympus to me, a bit supernatural. My body took all the heat it could, into the marrow, then I flopped out on a table and gazed at the rolling kelp bed below. Learned to distinguish the heads of seals and otters from the bulbous weed, feeling pink and vulnerable, a shrimp of being against the looming of that sea and the cooling wind. Had a limp feeling in me that can come in no other way—neither from wine nor weariness. Became simply a sentient noodle.

"There's no other way to be this way," one chap remarked. I lolled and knew he was right. An hour later the cold felt cold again, we dressed and turned in our towels. It wasn't until sometime the next morning that I lost that feeling of transparency and became hard and opaque again. Was it the hot water, discrete minerals, cold breeze or the mesmerizing kelp bed? Henry said only, "That's the hot springs for you."

Back in Santa Barbara during the following years—those were the house-building years, for many of us were involved with handmade houses—it became a Saturday night ritual to pile into a truck and visit the Las Cruces hot spring where muscles aching from the labor of bullying railroad ties, boulders and wheelbarrows were sweetly soothed in the hot mineral pool. There was the camraderie too. Thus hot springs soaking became a natural part of our lives and led eventually to the invention of the backyard hot tub.

But it wasn't until last spring, when Bill and Ruth Kaysing appeared with the germ of the great hot springs book, that I realized there were hundreds of places in the west where people could indulge in the pleasures of soaking. I was fully content with what Santa Barbara had to offer, but Bill, who must be part gypsy with the snooping instincts of a hound dog, was determined to seek out all the great hot springs.

Their journey began and postcards from Idaho, Oregon and Washington came, each one a little firecracker of enthusiasm. When they returned, in late November, with manuscript and photos, I was overwhelmed by the sheer exuberance of their wanderings, and the marvelous variety of hot spring environments—decaying old spa hotels in mountains, lonely water holes in the desert, hot natural streams in back woods.

Back to nature, back to water, back to peace within ourselves!

—LEON ELDER

INTRODUCTION

WHY HOT SPRINGS?

Imagine for a moment a peaceful valley . . . miles and miles from any habitation or twentieth century "civilization." For all you know, the year could be 1974 *B.C.* instead of A.D. In fact, the valley probably hasn't changed much in 4,000 years.

Outcroppings of granite and slate lend the appearance of a great natural monument. From a well-worn fissure where granite contacts slate, a stream of clear hot water gushes forth. At ten gallons a minute, the flow creates a pleasant, steaming brook that cascades down several rocky waterfalls. On either side, grasses and shrubs that have learned to tolerate the over-100-degree temperature grow in abundance. The water splashes down to a rustic flume nailed together from weathered planks. The water flows smoothly and silently through the flume to a natural pool lined with well-worn stones. The pool is four or five feet deep and perhaps seven feet square. Nearby, an aspen offers one of its older branches as a convenient hook for your clothes. Kick off those dusty boots and levis, strip off your other clothes and slide into that warm, soothing, mind- and body-relaxing

water. Beautiful? All hot springs lovers know that this sensation is one of the best that the world has to offer mortal man.

As you lie back wiggling your toes in a mild form of ecstacy, you'll probably meditate upon the great wisdom and inspired design that produced such a benevolent combination . . . the valley, the hot springs and you and your friends to enjoy it. Float awhile and gaze at the surrounding cottonwoods tinged with touches of yellow now that autumn is approaching. Below the pool a small stream of cold water gurgles by, its banks festooned with bright yellow and scarlet wildflowers . . . late bloomers that seem to defy the season. Amidst this natural beauty, with your body, mind and spirit at rest, you achieve a new awareness of the simple yet bountiful pleasures the world affords.

Fortunately, you can enjoy this pleasure quite easily. There are well over a thousand hot springs in Western America whose locations are presented in this book. It is possible that there may be hundreds more that are undiscovered or too small to attract the attention of a cataloger. This is possible because there are many thousands of miles of wilderness terrain, especially in the west, where travel has been minimal or non-existent. Last year, the authors discovered a hot spring in southeast Oregon that was not mentioned in the official U.S. Geological survey on the subject. Surprisingly, it had been well-developed at one time with wooden bathtubs and a bathhouse, but had long since fallen into disuse, consequent ruin, and anonymity.

Finding your own private hot spring could be an exciting adventure in your life. But whether you find one for yourself or visit one mentioned in the listings which follow, we guarantee that a hot spring will make your life more enjoyable. We suggest that you keep this book in your car, camper, plane, boat or backpack. Then as you travel, you'll be able to determine a route that will include one or more hot springs on your way.

We trust that this book will assist you in becoming a proficient hot spring user and, ultimately, a lover of natural warm baths who includes them in any travel itinerary. When you encounter an interesting location, write us care of the publisher. Send a photo, technical data and your own comments. We'll make every effort to include this expansion of knowledge in future editions of the book.

WHAT IS A HOT SPRING?

Ponderous textbooks on the subject define a hot spring as any spring or well whose water temperature is noticeably above the average ambient air temperature. This means that a "hot" spring could be as cool as 50°F, which, as a matter of fact, one is in Utah.

In Europe, commercially developed springs with temperatures above 20°C are classified as thermal In the United States, only those springs are called thermal or hot whose temperatures are at least 15°F above the mean annual temperature of the temperature of the air in their localities.

So much for textbooks. Most of the springs that are discussed in this book are well into the comfort zone. And some of them require plenty of cooling off in a pool before soaking.

ORIGINS

Where does this hot water originate? There are lots of theories. One of the most popular has surface water percolating down through channels to the lower levels of the earth where temperatures are much hotter. For example, at one mile beneath the surface, the temperature is about 85^0 hotter. At two miles the rocks are hot enough to boil water. If you are interested, at 25 miles below your feet at this moment, rocks are molten (2500^0F), so don't do anything rash now or later.

This heat stems from two major (and of course theoretical) sources: the kinetic energy that was transformed to heat energy when the earth was being created by parties not completely known to this writer, and radioactive elements that function in the same way as a nuclear reactor; i.e. heating effects through the decay of atomic structures.

Readings in books on alchemy and early Greek thought indicate that the ancients believed that certain horned people down below were having lost souls stoke up big fires. The residual heat provided lots of free hot water to those still alive and well on the surface. Dramatic but not totally believable. Here's a sketch which summarizes the most likely process:

A generalized illustration of a hot spring type of geothermal system, with high rate of upflow.

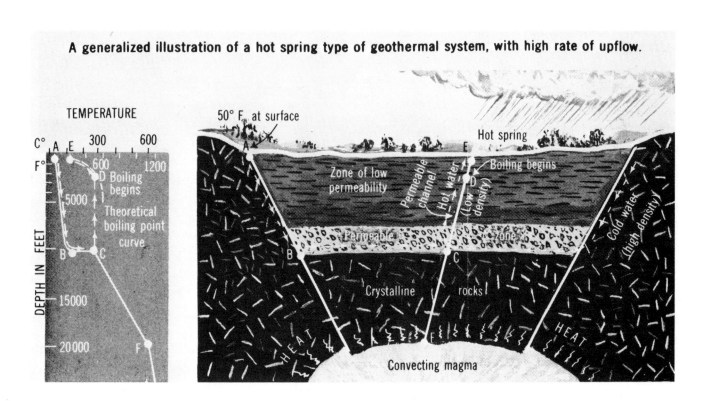

Big Caliente Hot Springs north of Santa Barbara is a good example of this type . . . in fact the sketch could easily describe the mechanism of this very attractive spring.

TYPES OF SPRINGS

There are as many varieties of hot springs as nature could provide. Although the great majority seem to follow the pattern just described, here are others of great strangeness. Diana's Punch Bowl in central Nevada is such a spring. At the present time, it resembles a symmetrical hill rising from a flat valley floor. No doubt it began as a surface spring and through the years has built its own "bowl" by carrying up various minerals with the hot water. Hot Lake in southeast Oregon is also typical of this self-buildup process. In centuries to come it may create very high sides . . . at present it is only a few feet above the surrounding desert. Some of the best examples of built-up springs appear in Yellowstone.

Although related to the basic spring type explained in the sketch, there are hot springs that emerge from *great* depths. Fales Hot Spring on the eastern slope of the Sierra Nevada is said to be more than 7,000 feet deep! The possibility of surface water percolating downward to this depth is less likely than an alternative—the water that gushes forth from Fales may be "new" water that has never been to the surface before. Theories abound as to the origin of this virgin water. It could be made fresh from the compression of rocks; rocks do contain entrapped water. Or, it could be generated from the combining of free hydrogen and oxygen deep within the earth. The same mystery surrounds another famous spring, not hot, but still fascinating. This is the giant spring that produces the Metolius River in central Oregon. Tens of thousands of gallons of pure, fresh, drinkable cool water gush forth from a rocky cave. To date, no one has been able to discover the source. Small amounts of tracer chemicals have been introduced into water supplies for miles around but none has ever appeared in the Metolius spring. Thus, many hot springs, emerging from great and unknown depths, could have as their source some yet undiscovered process.

UNUSUAL SPRINGS

Seventy-five acres of hot springs? Yes, that's what you'll find if you journey to Ward's Springs in Township 34 north, Range 23 East at the northwest end of Alkali Flat in northwest Nevada. Take your choice of lukewarm and tepid to boiling.

Although it is subject to changes, especially over the winter months, the Little Caliente Spring just north of Mono campground above Santa Barbara can be regulated. A small creek runs most of the year just above the outflow of the small hot spring. When we were last there, someone installed a pipe that allowed the cold water to flow over the small pool. Thus, a bather could let temperature build up in the pool and when it rose too high, simply let some cold water flow in.

Temperature control is also possible when the hot springs flows down a small canyon. A series of small pools can be built, each one slightly cooler as the water descends. Capra Hot Springs in central Oregon is a good example of this principle.

Did you say 75,000 gallons a minute? Yes, this is the flowrate of a fantastic spring in southern Oregon near the village of Summer Lake. Although not truly a hot spring, the 66°F water was beautifully swimmable in the summertime when we visited. Most of the water wells up from beneath a large lake and pours into a pool through a conduit. Other springs gush forth from a cliff face festooned with jungle-like bushes, grass and flowers.

SOME BACKGROUND

Back in the late nineteenth century and up until the 1930's, hot springs resorts were very fashionable in this country. "Taking the cure" was a custom which many people of foreign extraction brought over with them from the old country. Europeans have for centuries had great faith in the curative properties of thermal spring water and great spas are to be found all over Europe which have retained their popularity to this day. The cure often consisted in daily soaks in hot pools, additional therapy through the application of hot mud from the area, and many glasses of the spring water guzzled internally for whatever good works could be wrought by its benevolent chemicals.

Europeans were not unique in this practice. A brief study of the history of almost all of the hot springs visited by the authors revealed that America's first inhabitants frequented hot springs long before the white man muscled in. Whenever a spring was taken over by an entrepreneur for development as a resort, dozens of Indian artifacts were invariably uncovered in the area around the spring.

So perhaps our European forebearers or Indian hosts knew something that is just now experiencing a rediscovery by the newly emerging coterie of hot spring devotees. Undoubtedly the back-to-the-land movement has aided in this discovery. So while we make no claims for the medicinal or curative values of these thermal springs of the west, we rejoice in their renaissance. If nothing else, they are a palliative for city-wrought ills, a soother of the troubled sprit, a purgative for the poisoned mind and body and a source of supreme delight.

HOT SPRINGS EQUIPMENT

What do you need to visit a hot spring? Exactly nothing is the correct answer. To illustrate: alone or on occasion with a friend, I would ride my trusty 250cc Maico trail/scramble motorcycle back to Big Caliente. Just before arrival, clothes would be zipped off so that the second the bike was leaned against the dressing room, it was zoom—splash, into the hot tub!

The moral: you don't *need* anything to enjoy the salubrious effect of natural warm waters swirling over your tired, 20th-century-tormented body. You may *want* a few items to ensure greater comfort, and that we'll discuss presently. However, the most important thing is a friend or friends. Beyond these are sundries only. So here's a review of equipment that could make your hot springing more comfortable and enjoyable.

You won't need them at developed springs, but often a pair of zoris or sandals will keep the sharp mineral spikes and assorted thorny thingies out of your tender feet. They are also useful for wading around in shallow hot lakes.

A thick towel is handy for drying off to prevent chilling if breezes blow. It's also useful to put down as a mat for a leisurely snooze.

There are hot springs that have oozy edges— mud, muck, guck and other squashy stuff that makes walking difficult. Thus, the true hot springs lover will probably carry a few lengths of thin, waterproof plywood along to place as a temporary trail. The same pieces of wood could be used to create an impromptu wharf at the edge of some otherwise difficult-to-use hot spring.

Desert hot springs are pleasant to use any time of the year but you may want to bring a piece of canvas or cloth to act as a sunshade. Much handier to pack away than a pokey umbrella.

Quite a few hot springs are located in cattle country. Sometimes you'll have to go through gates (get permission if applicable) and you'll be in with some large animals—bulls and cows and such. So bring some courage, light feet and perhaps an old bugle to blow to scare them away. We've never had any trouble with animals even though they often hang around the hot pools as watering places. We wish you, dear readers, the same luck.

A fine wine, mellow cheese, tasty sausage, and a crusty loaf of french sourdough go well anywhere in the world, but they seem to blend best with a tranquil, outasite hot spring. So by all means, bring some snacks and eatables. We recall a festive time when the visitors to a popular hot spring simply shared all their vins and viands.

Staying overnight or nights? Then bring sleeping bags, pads and perhaps a small tent, unless you're fortunate enough to own a trailer or camper. And don't worry about the cold. The most pleasant experience of your life is still ahead unless you've done this—leaped out of your freezing sleeping bag in the middle of the night and jumped naked into a really hot spring. Now *that* is an experience that defies all descriptions!

Technically oriented or just plain curious? Then include a quart container and a thermometer in your gear. With the former you can measure the flow rate of springs that don't run too fast. The time in seconds to fill a quart bottle divided into 15 will give you the gallons per minute. Compare with the book just for kicks and let us know if there's a big discrepancy. Leave the bottle full, if you have a chemist friend. He'll give you the analysis of mineral good things therein. Which is a good place for a mild warning. Don't drink too much water from a hot spring. Many of them contain dissolved arsenic and other poisons.

An old kerosene lantern (never one of those hissing, eye-destroying Coleman gasoline things, please), a guitar or harmonica, and a flagon of aged brandy would complete any hot springs aficionado's list of good things to take.

THE GREAT & NEAR-GREAT

CALIFORNIA

BYRON HOT SPRINGS

The faded glories of hot springs resorts is almost too well exemplified by this facility which combines decay with new growth. Once the mecca for wealthy tourists from the Bay Area, its buildings now are falling into disrepair furthered by the pronouncements of the county inspectors as being "unsafe." However, the present owners believe that with a lot of money and energy, Byron can and should be restored. They are working diligently to find a new source of hot water, the old flows having ceased due to a falling water table. Thus far they have created a large lake which, while not warm, is beautifully swimmable. They intend to restore some of the original bathhouses which are well worth visiting for their walls of beautiful white Italian marble. Some of the many old buildings on the premises are being refurbished as living quarters for residents and a fairly hip transient population. The young couple who now own Byron Hot Springs have made the premises available on a no-charge basis to anyone who wishes to make use of the lake for swimming and fishing or enjoy a picnic lunch in the attractively maintained park-like area between the buildings.

Early Spanish explorers found Indians living near Byron and there are curious artifacts to be found. It has been conjectured that the Indians associated the springs with the supernatural and offered carved bones and stones as sacrifices to the spirit of the waters.

Probably the first Anglo-American to use the springs was an unknown traveler who, in the dead of winter, was surprised to find hot water bubbling up through the frozen ground. After enlarging the opening of the spring, bathing and proceeding on greatly invigorated, he no doubt told others of the marvelous waters.

It's an easy place to find, since it is approximately halfway between San Francisco and Stockton. Driving east from San Francisco on Highway 4, you'll reach Brentwood. Signs in this community indicate Byron as being only a few miles further southeast. If you approach from Highway 99 in the Stockton area, take Highway 4 west out of Stockton and look for the signs pointing to Byron about 4 miles after crossing Old River.

BIG CALIENTE

It's just the right distance from Montecito, a suburb of Santa Barbara. The twenty miles or so by dirt road is sufficiently long so that when you return you know you've been on a trip (in every sense of the word), but short enough so that it's possible to leave early from work—say around three p.m., drive or ride over and still be back in time for dinner.

The best way to go is by motorcycle. First you will climb through heavily wooded—oaks and sycamores—Romero Canyon, passing Robert Maynard Hutchins' fabulous estate at the mouth of the canyon. Turning left off the only paved section, you'll climb steeply over a weather-worn road. Within a mile or two you'll cross a couple of gurgling brooks—at least they gurgle in the summertime. Suddenly as you make a lefthand sweeping turn, a spectacular view of Santa Barbara County coastline will be revealed to your grateful eyes. On clear days you'll see the coastline south of Ventura and islands like San Miguel more than fifty miles off shore. (Just ignore those ugly oil towers and keep the good thought on the day when they will be removed and the people who brought them there won't be around any longer.)

Continuing on up towards Romero Saddle you'll find secret wooded places where tiny streams gush forth from hidden springs. The road steepens and becomes rockier and those with vertigo have a chance to exercise that feeling . . . at one point the road drops off to a sheer 800-foot cliff. But a little farther on, you'll be rewarded; a wide part of the road is a perfect vista point for you to park your machine and overlook the red-roofed city of Santa Barbara, its harbor and surrounding hills—the fabled la tienda adorada, as the Spanish knew it.

After you've feasted your eyes on this sweeping scene, leap back aboard your trusty trail motorcycle or scooter and zoom up and over Romero Saddle. There a more primitive, totally natural vista greets your eyes . . . the ranges of the Los Padres, each one higher than the last, climbing ultimately to nearly 7,000-foot Big Pine Mountain. (It's becoming obvious that this trip to a hot springs is more than just a trip to a hot springs . . . it's an adventure, a challenge and a great treat for those who enjoy the best in outdoor scenery.)

From the Saddle the road descends in a series of loops and straightaways to the Santa Ynez River Valley. Take the time to stop for some blissful moments at Escondido Canyon, a heavily wooded copse with an all-year brook splashing and sparkling through. As you continue downwards, there will be tantalizing glimpses of the sinuous Santa Ynez River winding around ancient bluffs. Soon, your wheels will be washed by the rushing (in winter) or gentle (in summer) waters of the historically interesting Santa Ynez River.

Then, delight of delights . . . you'll follow the river's course on an adjacent road for several miles. Suddenly the valley widens to meadowland dotted with giant oaks and ancient sycamores. Just beyond is the Forestry Service Station at Pendola. Although you'll be tempted to ride on down the river, turn right here and follow Big Caliente Creek for a couple of miles through an equally beautiful California canyon. As the walls of the canyon narrow, you'll cross the creek twice. Then a fast right turn will deliver you to the Big Caliente Hot Spring area.

The powers that be have built their typically ugly but substantial concrete block house, johns and changing facilities. But don't let these architectural monstrosities lessen your joy with the natural offerings . . . 118 degree water full of skin-soothing soda compounds that flows into a well-used concrete tub. There is a valve that you can regulate to change the temperature of the water. If it's too hot, shut off the flow and let the water cool. Conversely, if it's a nippy day in November, turn the faucet on full and let it gush forth the soothing waters.

Oftentimes you'll be the only guest, especially during the week. On weekends you'll have lots of company, the kind that you'll enjoy rapping with and perhaps sharing your fried chicken, crusty french bread and bota. The tub has been the scene of hundreds, yea thousands of impromptu, good-vibes parties. Your writer counts some of these experiences among his most treasured memories. One time someone piped the excess water to a free-flowing, high-spurting shower. The totally naked, spiritually free boys and girls, men and women, cycled between the hot tub, the shower spray and the icy creek that flows just a few feet below the hot spring pool. Such gaiety, such merriment—joy that should adorn a freshly made Grecian urn.

There is a philosophy to Big Caliente that probably applies as well to similar hot springs. Slide into the lovely water slowly until all but your head is immersed. Let this natural balm soak away your cares and ease your tense muscles. But don't soak more than a few minutes at a time or you may find that you are somewhat weak. So leap out periodically for a quick splashing romp in the creek or a mad chase around the bathhouse or even perhaps a brief snooze in the bright sunlight at the edge of the pool. Later you may want to wander upstream finding a glade of rough-barked, shimmery-leafed cottonwoods, rounded boulders and clear waters flowing over white sand and multi-colored river pebbles. At this point, if you look up the hillside to your right you'll see an area of intense green . . . the lush grass that surrounds the portals of the Big Caliente spring itself. If you are a genuine hot springs aficionado, you'll leap lightly from rock to rock and ascend the steep hillside. You'll be rewarded by the sight of hot, clear water gushing from rocky crevices, emitting wisps of steam and lining the channel with freshly dissolved minerals. Muse there for a moment— let your mind spin backwards a few centuries and you'll see near-naked Chumash Indians cavorting about in rudely fashioned pools both at the source and at the nearby streamside. There's an old one, a retired chief, soaking his 90-year-old bones with a beatific expression on his brown, wrinkled face.

The more adventuresome will enjoy a walk up Big Caliente Canyon to a high dam built to entrap silt to prevent it from wandering down to one of Santa Barbara's drinking water reservoirs several miles away. Here you'll see water falling about sixty feet to a deep and, in the summer, swimmable cold water pool. Further wanderings will reveal the wilderness that the Los Padres Forest features in abundance. But back again to Big Caliente for a last pleasant dip. Then on with clothes and urban cares and the return trip to town.

LITTLE CALIENTE

The designers of Santa Barbara's back country were especially generous with hot water. Less than seven miles by winding, scenic, tree-festooned roads, there is to be found the sister to Big Caliente. As you double back to the Pendola Guard Station, make a right and travel on down alongside the faithful Santa Ynez River. En route you'll pass some friendly campgrounds, places where the road dips down almost into the sandy riverbed, and then you'll ascend an escarpment that separates the Santa Ynez from the Mono River. Oaks become thicker at this point along with cottonwoods and sycamores. Soon you'll see Mono campground to your left and another silt retention dam. That sounds prosaic as you read it but, actually, the swimming hole below Mono dam has been the scene of many Tom Sawyer/Huck Finn/Becky Thatcher gatherings. Each year the pool changes depending on the frivolities of the river itself. But to continue on . . . pass the campground, keep to your right and within two miles you'll be stopped by a locked gate leading to the Ogilvy Ranch. Park here and walk about 100 yards to the right. As with the Mono swimming hole, Little Caliente changes from season to season. Sometimes it's merely a muddy little pond; at other times it's a well organized, clear pool with temperature control. Actually, this is one of the great sports attendant to hot springing . . . you never know what you'll find. More secluded and private than Big Caliente, this small, natural spa has been the center of many farout gatherings as native Santa Barbarans will confess. We hope that it will remain for many years to provide you and your friends with a warm water environment for getting it all together.

OH MY GOD HOT SPRINGS

In the Anza-Borrego Desert, 140 miles southeast of Los Angeles, is a hot springs which does not appear on any map. It was named by a small band of hot springs explorers who had heard many rumors of its existence. Late one night, after many hours of searching under the hot desert sun, they heard the gurgling of hot, flowing, acrid sulphur water. This sound, audible in the still night, evoked the exclamation: "Oh my God, oh my God, we've found it!"

Apparently, some years ago a person drilling for drinking water found instead a deposit of hot sulphur water. He capped the spring with metal casing and abandoned it. At a later date someone else who chanced upon the metalwork, pierced it, al-lowing the hot water to flow out across the sand. Over the years other industrious visitors have dug a teardrop-shaped pool in which the water can collect. This hot spring pool in the middle of an otherwise worthless and barren desert creates a landscape with a strong surrealistic quality.

The temperature of the water as it flows out of the metal casing is approximately 140°, but due to the relatively slow outflow, the water cools to 90° at the end of the pool. In the heat of the desert afternoon, the hot waters of the pool seem rather inhospitable; however, a soak in the chill of the evening, under a clear, star-filled sky, is an experience of incomparable beauty.

(Photo and text contributed by Leonard Koren)

19

KELLY'S HOT SPRINGS

A flow of 325 gallons a minute would be a healthy output for a cold spring. However, when it comes out heated to nearly boiling, that has to be called a really fine, generous hot spring. And that's exactly what you'll find at currently defunct Kelly's Hot Spring, located on the main highway (299) four miles northeast of Canby. In case Canby doesn't ring a bell, it's 18 miles southwest of Alturas. In the event that Alturas is a stranger in your inventory of towns, this 3,000-soul community is in Modoc County in the extreme northeast corner of California.

As we wandered through the shambles that was once a bustling and no-doubt profitable hot springs resort, our minds mused upon the possibilities of resurrecting this bountiful natural resource. Upon inquiry we found that it is for sale and can be purchased with or without several hundred acres of land nearby. There is an old building teetering on the brink between restoration and a match.

An old swimming pool is also on the borderline. A number of other old cottages and sheds lean in the direction of the bulldozer's touch. But the decay of human artifacts does not extend to the huge blue, bubbling pool that roils and rustles as boiling water from the depths surges to the surface in a true artesian flow. At present, the heat of this water goes entirely to waste . . . a great tragedy since it could be used not only as recreation or therapy, it is possible to employ it as the medium to heat hydroponic hothouses. This is being done at a hot springs nearby. The water cools slowly as it wends its way towards a large reservoir on the southern part of the property.

So collect an investment group. Take over this marvelous natural spring and then thousands of people would be able to enjoy it once again. We see it as a fly-in, drive-in resort, plus use as an all-year round vegetable and fruit growing agricultural venture.

Like one of Doré's paintings in Dante's "Inferno", the boiling bubbling waters of Kelly's Hot Springs flow at more than 350 gallons per minute.

GROVER HOT SPRINGS

If you are in the Lake Tahoe vicinity, take a pleasant side trip down to Markleeville, an hour or so to the south. Then a four mile ride thru Ponderosa pines will find you arriving at a well-maintained (by the Forestry Service) hot springs. There are two pools, the warmer one is shown, the larger is held at about 80 degrees and great for vigorous swimming. An unusual feature is the use of the hot water to warm the floors of the bathhouses. Take time to walk about the pools to where the several springs gush forth from the earth. Also enjoy the surroundings . . . great meadows edged by tall evergreens.

There's a campground nearby so plan to stay a while. Small fees, well worth it.

Grover Hot Springs in virtually uninhabited Alpine County usually has a customer or two. Although there's a small fee payable to the forest ranger in attendance, it's well worth it.

BROCKWAY

Hot springs, like cats, often have more than one life. This one, located in the fantastically beautiful north-shore country of Lake Tahoe, is being resurrected from slow decay by the building of an expensive and well-planned condominium. Once known as Carnelian Springs, the hot waters flow from beneath the lake; thus the building of the coffer dams to avoid mixing with the chill, 50 degree waters of Tahoe. There are a total of six springs with temperatures of from 120 to 140°F and a substantial flow rate . . . nearly three barrels per minute.

Steam rises from these "ancient" concrete tubs at Brockway Hot Springs. That's beautiful blue Lake Tahoe directly beyond.

HOT CREEK

A most intelligent design . . . a nearly boiling spring located in the bed of an icy creek. The scalding water emerges in a strong flow and tempers the 40^{0}F waters that sweep down from the frigid slopes of the eastern Sierras. Thus, you may enjoy almost any temperature you wish, from near ice water to heat that would cook a potato.

It's a most unusual feeling to swim about in the rather deep and swiftly flowing creek and sense the swiftly changing temperatures—invigorating too.

Among the other features of this thermal phenomenon is the row of small geysers near the foot bridge, the outcroppings of volcanic rock and a well-built bath house and parking lot above the creek. No fees. Stay as long as you like.

CAMPBELL HOT SPRINGS

Near Sierraville, Calif., this resort has the distinction of surviving for nearly 120 years. There are individual baths at over a 100^{0}F and a large pool maintained at about 80^{0}F. Facilities include a bar, restaurant, hotel and camping facilities.

PARAISO HOT SPRINGS

This venerable resort has welcomed visitors for many decades. Located just outside the sleepy, good vibes town of Soledad, California (there's a fine Mexican bakery there), Paraiso has the amenities of a fully-equipped resort. You can enjoy the tranquility of the Salinas valley, Steinbeck country; the views of the Gabilans to the east and Santa Lucias to the west.

Gradually falling into ruin, the old café at Kelly's Hot Springs lies abandoned.

A hot springs that falls into the category of older but still well maintained is Keough near Bishop, California. The 127^{0}F water is trickled through a cooling tower to reduce its temperature before admitting it to a 100 by 40 foot pool. Minerals include various sodas that are helpful to the kidneys according to legend.

KEENE WONDER SPRINGS

Death Valley is full of surprises—year 'round fish in the Armagosa River, huge stones that seem to move by themselves, a "devil's golf course" and for thermal springs lovers, Keene Wonder Springs not too far north of Furnace Creek Ranch.

To see it involves following a couple-mile jaunt down a typically rough desert sideroad. But for those who relate to rocks as well as water, it will be a most rewarding trek. Strange formations of what appears to be coral burst thru the sands in great abundance. But back to the springs: when you approach the foothills, look for a rusty pipeline that once linked the springs with the Keene Wonder Mine. Turn left, by car or on foot and follow the remains of the pipe. Soon you'll see traces of moisture, then trickles, and finally you'll hear a steady flow of water from the lower pool. Take the time to pursue the stream further and you'll find a curious geological phenomenon—a hot creek flowing underground. It may be viewed with reasonable safety from the mouth of a vertical shaft.

Not really a swimming type of springs, Keene still has the quality of strangeness, an other-world uniqueness, that will round out your total hot spring experience. And don't forget to look back down Death Valley itself—that view alone makes the Keene Wonder Spring a worthwhile addition to your itinerary.

OREGON

If you look at the map of Oregon you'll notice that the majority of the hot springs are concentrated in the southeast and south central region. Most of them are still in their natural state for the obvious reason that this part of Oregon is sparsely inhabited. A typical county might have 10,000 residents to fill up 10,000 square miles. So exploration is of the freest kind. As long as you have a dependable vehicle with good tires, you'll have no problems. And even if you do, the people are friendly and accommodating. For example, we were traveling from Frenchglen to Fields along what has to be one of the most sparsely traveled roads in the west, and casually waved at a low flying plane. Without hesitation the pilot banked, descended steeply and landed on the road just behind us. We were quite embarrassed recognizing that our friendly wave had been interpreted as a call for help. But the event ended well because the pilot and his friend had wanted to chat anyway and were curious to know what we were doing so far away from anyplace with such a large trailer.

So feel completely free to wander about this big sky country and discover some of its many hot springs on your own. We found a number with most unusual characteristics and/or comforts and here's our review.

Breitenbush Hot Springs.

Once a popular place for the farmers and their families in Paradise Valley, Vale Hot Springs now falls into ruin under the hot Oregon sun.

Water vapor rises from one of the several hot lakes at this well-cared-for resort and retirement center. A conventional pool is at left.

VALE

While there are many hot springs that could be developed throughout the western United States, many lack the nearby population center that could ensure their success. The old Vale hot springs in eastern Oregon near the cluster of towns surrounding Boise, Idaho, could be redeveloped. For sure, you'd be starting from just about point zero. Our visit there revealed only a gradually deteriorating bathhouse and a somewhat decayed but potentially restorable pool. While there is no evidence of the hot waters which once filled the pool, it is possible that the springs could be restored by drilling. In the U.S. Government book on western hot springs, Vale is described as once having a flow rate of 20 gallons a minute and a temperature of almost 200 degrees. The book also mentions a well 140 feet deep, so it is possible that the water was once pumped up for pool use.

Although restoration might be a bit farfetched, the existence of tens of thousands of people within easy driving distance, makes the possibilities at least mildly exciting. If all of this interests you, drive to Vale, it's 12 miles west of Ontario, Oregon, and take a look for yourself.

SUMMER LAKE HOT SPRINGS

First locate either Bend or Lakeview on your Oregon map. If it's Bend, let your eye travel south on 97 to the junction with 31. Then angling southeast, you'll encounter a large blue area labeled Summer Lake. Traveling north from Lakeview on 395, you would encounter 31 just south of Lake Abert, a strange and mysterious almost unworldly body of water that we will discuss in another book titled GREAT SWIMMING HOLES OF THE WEST.

Whichever direction you take, the relaxed and easygoing, faraway from everything Summer Lake Hot Springs will be clearly evident from a sign on the east side of the road.

A couple of decades ago, Summer Lake was close to being a ruin. But along came Jeff and Glenda McDaniel, a friendly pair of native Oregonians, who rebuilt everything to its present state of neat and trim orderliness. The pool itself is roofed over to protect it from the hurricane-like winds of winter. You'll find a place to change and shower and the pool itself, though modest in size, has a bone-relaxing 102 degree all-year temperature. You'll be able to see the approximately 20 gallon per minute flow as it bubbles into the pool from a pipe that is connected to an artesian well. While tourists are relatively scarce, local residents find the pool a good place to gather for gossip and easing of the minimal cares of this rural region that simply lets the rest of the world go by.

Cattle graze peacefully about the grassy grounds and you can wander yourself and explore the three springs that comprise Summer Lake. Without too much persuasion, Glenda will probably show you a fascinating collection of Indian artifacts. As with most hot springs, the original owners of America frequented this spring and left behind such artifacts as arrowheads, stone knives and grinding equipment. Glenda said that after the winter rains, new arrowheads are exposed, so if you're lucky you may find one for yourself.

This building houses the indoor pool at Summer Lake. Surplus water flows into the small pond at far left.

ANA HOT SPRINGS

Very convenient to Summer Lake is one of the largest (in terms of flow rate) hot springs in the western United States. Ana Springs gushes out of several places in the desert at the almost unbelievable rate of from to 50,000 to 75,000 gallons per minute!!! To get there, drive north two miles from the Summer Lake post office and turn right at a sign which says "Ana Reservoir". After about a mile, you'll notice a large lake on your right. Turn down any of the dirt roads leading in that direction and you'll find a camping ground equipped with fire pits, wood (at least while we were there) and a Chic Sale. At first the springs won't be evident and feeling the water will reveal that this is one of the cooler hot springs . . . ambient temperature is in the high sixties. But as you turn left from the lake, you'll suddenly find a miniature version of the Grand Canyon into which gush the enormous quantities of water that comprise the spring. Most of it comes from an ordinary galvanized pipe about three feet in diameter, but there are also several natural springs which leap out of fissures in the canyon wall. Heavy growth of various trees and shrubs almost conceals some of the spring outlets, but a little probing around will be most rewarding, especially in the spring and summer when colorful wild flowers festoon the grotto.

Frankly, this place blew our everloving minds mainly because the beauty, sound and magnificence seem to relate to another place, another planet, another time. Although a few apparently harmless snakes were slithering around, I couldn't resist throwing off my clothes and leaping into the refreshing water while Ruthie recorded the mad doings. It was great sport to try to swim against the current of thousands of gallons of water pouring into this fantastic pool. Try it yourself . . . you'll be amazed.

Close up of just one of the myriads of gushing inlets at Ana Springs. Note wildflowers at right.

What a great swimming hole! Not as hot as many hot springs, the water at 60°F is still considered to be thermal since it is significantly than the average annual air temperature. In the background, wildflowers festoon the spring-studded canyon walls.

CAPRA SPRINGS

While wandering about in the wilds of central Oregon south of the McKenzie River, we stumbled upon a fantastic spring, festooned with bits of old ponderosa bark, wildflowers and hippies . . . really students from the University of Oregon at nearby Eugene. We found the springs unnamed and thus bestowed upon it the name of our friendly publisher.

Capra is one of those new miraculous entities that make you certain of intelligent design work being manifested on earth. The spring originates in the exact center of a small creek. Thus, the hot water that gushes forth joins with the cold creek water to create just the right temperature for bathing. In addition, the water descends to three separate pools, so that the visitor is able to select a temperature close to his heart's desire. As if that weren't enough, all about Capra Springs are huge evergreens, giant grey granite boulders and permeating the region is the feeling of freedom that only the great outdoors can bestow.

We enjoyed chatting with the several young people who were bathing in the pools. They told us that it is a place that can be enjoyed practically all year since the roads are plowed. One young man commented on how delightful it was to trudge through powder snow and then leap into the warm waters that flow 24 hours a day.

After our refreshing hot bath which ranged from the topmost pool at about 115 degrees to an icy pool created by damming a part of the icy stream. We wandered about through the fir and redwood trees. We found several primitive camps with simple shelters shielding sleeping bags, guitars and food supplies from the elements. Many of the campers were visiting for extended periods of time and apparently there are no objections from the powers that claim to be.

There are other natural attractions nearby. About a quarter of a mile below the springs is a small lake offering good swimming in the summertime. The water is partly heated by the descending hot water from Capra Springs. Just across the road is Cougar Reservoir, an immense body of water created by damming the South Fork of the McKenzie River. We saw a few fishermen and water skiers, which indicated that these sports are available for the taking.

To reach this multi-recreational hot spring-outdoor sports area, take a right turn off highway 126, which goes east from Eugene along the McKenzie River, at the sign "Cougar Reservoir". When you come to the dam itself, turn right and drive about three miles at which point you will see the smaller lake appearing on your right. If it has a waterfall on its southern shore, it's the right one. Park your car or burro on the left side of the road and walk back to where a trail begins on the north side of the small lake. Follow this trail for about a quarter of a mile. Hiking shoes are recommended since some of the trail is steep and slippery. A good way to find it, is to simply stop and listen for the murmur of voices, happy shouts and the musical sound of water descending over rocks.

Indian-like shelters are built by lovers of the warm water at Capra Spring in central Oregon.

BELKNAP HOT SPRINGS

If Capra Springs proved too primitive for you, jump on your old burro or fire up the bug and drive six miles east of the village of McKenzie Bridge. Here you'll see a sign pointing towards Belknap Hot Springs, which has a healthy natural flow of 75 gallons per minute from several springs with temperatures varying from 147 to 180 degrees

New owners have done a dandy job of installing an elegant pool (the water gushes out of a handsome fixture), trailer spaces and accommodations for visitors in cottages. Prices are reasonable for what is offered . . . a comfortable, no-problem, fully developed hot spring resort.

HUNTER'S LODGE

More for viewing than bathing, this hot springs resort has more emphasis on skiing in the winter than it does on its bountiful hot water resources. But then this is typical of the current underuse of hot springs in general.

But there's lots to see at Hunter's Lodge. A large lake with swimmable water features the world's largest continuous geyser. It spurts boiling water high into the air every ten seconds. It's a spectacular display which allows you to have the feeling of Old Faithful without bucking the crowds of Yellowstone. One of the lakes freezes over in winter and the brochure shows happy skaters. While we were there, the natural hot water pool was not in use but since things change quickly in our present-day world, it could be open for business by the time readers of this book arrive there. There's plenty of lodging in comfortable rooms and, as we mentioned, spectacular skiing in the winter in Warner Canyon, just ten minutes to the east. For those who like the boards as well as hot springs, it sounds like a great combination. There are three 800-foot tows in tandem.

Ruth says to be sure and take along some bread crusts or corn to feed the myriad mallard and domestic ducks that abound on the Hunter's Lodge lakes and ponds.

Termed the most active geyser in America, this one at Hunter's Lodge spouts forth every ten or twenty seconds.

The outflow from Crane hot springs produces this picturesque little hot stream that Ruth is checking for boiled fish.

CRANE HOT SPRINGS

Although this very hot spring (126°F) is known officially as Crane, we call it the "no-return laundromat". Prior to leaping in, I tossed in my shorts and teeshirt for a quick laundry job. They promptly disappeared into the depths and the water was too hot either to bathe or try to retrieve them. Not a particularly easy hot springs to find, it is still intriguing with its grassy banks, small outlet stream wandering out into the desert and background of browsing bovines. Now if we could just build a small pool, let the water cool . . .

The large pool and owner's storybook-like house at Hidaway. This hot spring was so perfect, it's possible we only imagined it. Check us out some time.

HIDAWAY HOT SPRINGS

Remember when you were a small child and you read fairy stories with their "too perfect" illustrations: houses, neat, trim, painted an unbelievable white, the grass around them cropped to velvety green smoothness; creeks with perfect banks lined with wildflowers, and springs hot, cold or champagne gurgling out of colorful rock formations. And above all, an improbably blue sky with cottonball clouds.

If you don't think that places like this really exist, then come with us on a tour of an almost mythical hot springs, appropriately called Hidaway.

The first step is to locate the tiny town of Ukiah, which is about 27 miles north of the Middle Fork of the John Day River on Highway 395. (If you visited Ritter, Ukiah isn't more than a 45 minute drive away.) Turn east through Ukiah and go exactly 14 miles. You'll see a sign as you turn right that says Willoughby Springs with a small white sign that announces Hidaway. From then on the route is well-marked to the springs themselves. They are privately owned by a gentleman named

Holly Bean who spends his summers there. When we arrived in mid-August, we found no one around but since the usual keep-out signs were lacking, we knocked on the door to ask permission. With no one in sight and no one to answer our knock, we succumbed to the temptation of every hot springs lover, slipped off our clothes and slid into the 80-degree water of the large and immaculate pool. Ah, paradise!

The large pool is surrounded by smaller pools which have a higher temperature since they receive the first flow from the springs. We guessed the flow rate at about ten gallons a minute and the outlet temperature at about 105⁰F.

While we were basking in the delicious water, two friends of the owner arrived and joined us. We got the feeling that the owner was fairly relaxed about people using the spring in his absence. However, as with any piece of private property, it is advisable to make an effort to obtain permission before using even a spring as irresistible as Hidaway. We are going to give up trying to describe the place and leave it up to the rather inarticulate photographs in the hopes readers may see this lovely place at least once in their lifetime.

31

Shouts of joy echo from the usually busy hot spring pool at Lehman Springs in northeast Oregon. This busy resort draws people from as far away as Portland.

LEHMAN HOT SPRINGS

If for any reason you can't make the scene at Hidaway, don't be disappointed because there's an extremely public, well-developed spring not far away. To reach it, drive east on the road that you took into Hidaway and look for a sign that says Lehman Springs. They are about midway between Ukiah and Starkey and usually show on Oregon maps.

Lehman is the kind of place that you go to with a trailer or camper and a back seat full of kids. The day we arrived it would have been difficult to shoehorn one more youngster into the well-packed pool. There's places to park your recreational vehicle, a coffee shop and lots of wooded terrain for happy hiking between dips in the pool. Be sure to check the interesting, historical photos showing Lehman in years past. They are on the walls of the coffee shop.

We were well received and informed by the genial manager who took the time to show us the source of the springs and his special method of temperature control. Lehman is open all year and deserves its popularity with Oregonians and out of state visitors alike.

Performing the temperature test on the scalding creek that delivers water to the Lehman pool.

HOT LAKE

Want to take a trip into the 1920's as well as visit a hot spring? Then travel about ten miles south of La Grande, Oregon You won't have any trouble finding the place, as clouds of steam rise from the big lake which gives this resort its name. Also, you'll see the huge, comfortable old hotel which has been in business for many years. Walk into the hotel with us for a moment. There's a giant lobby with rocking chairs, the latest newspapers, books and magazines. No one cares if you sit down to relax for a while . . . in fact, we were completely ignored. When we finally approached the desk to gather some basic information, members of the staff were hospitable but reluctant to break up their animated discussion about how to run the place.

All about is an air of genteel, permissible decay. It's not difficult to imagine that Hot Lake really jumped as a resort early in the twentieth century.

Now, it appears to function mainly as an antideluvian sanitarium and old folks home. Rates are reasonable in case you want to stay a few years.

Outside we found the same relaxed environment . . . a friendly goose plucked bread crusts from Ruthie's hands; no one objected to my prowling around a strange building that had a hot springs grotto within. There was even a huge old cast iron ladle, no doubt intended for use as an egg boiler.

As you wander about the grounds, 180 degree water seems to belch forth from many sources. This is understandable when you consider that a quarter of a million gallons of mineral water gush forth every 24 hours! Besides sulphur, the hot water contains calcium, aluminum, magnesium sulphate, sulphides, phosphorus and iron. The present managers believe that the mineral content is useful in the treatment of rheumatism, arthritis, neuritis and kindred ailments.

Meanwhile, inside a rather strange building co-intrepid hot springs hunter, Wild Bill Kaysing checks out a hardboiled egg cooker at a boiling spring tub.

SODA LAKE

If you continue south from Frenchglen, which is approximately 50 miles south of Burns, you'll eventually cross the mysterious Steens Mountains and descend into the minute but fascinating village of Fields. Gasoline, groceries and other supplies are available from a most accommodating couple who purchased the entire community and live there as though the rest of the world didn't even exist.

From Fields, turn north for approximately 10 miles until you see Alvord Lake. It may be dry or after a rainfall may contain water. About two and a half miles south of this lake, check for a road which turns right. It's rather bumpy and there's not much clearance for modern cars, but we made it in a '66 Chevy Impala, which proves it's not too bad. After a mile or so, you'll see evidence of the old borax works which once existed here. Especially unique is a cabin constructed of blocks of almost pure borax. Near this cabin you won't be able to miss sighting the approximately five-acre lake of water about 90 degrees F. Although it's somewhat difficult to navigate the squashy ground, crystallized mineral bank and squishy mud of the shallows, once you find yourself floating in Soda lake it will be worth all of your troubles. Just imagine swimming in clear warm water that rises from great depths at a flow rate of nearly a thousand gallons a minute. To us it was like a visit to another planet circling within a distant galaxy.

With a small amount of work, a pier could be built from the shore using some of the abandoned timbers and boards lying about. With this modest improvement, a hot lake would be acceptable even to those of a marginally intrepid nature. There are hot springs that are easier to find and negotiate foot-wise, but it's difficult to recall one that God built on such a gargantuan scale.

The shoreline has been built up over the centuries by deposits of various minerals.

As you approach Soda Lake near Fields, Oregon, you'll find this curious landmark: a worker's hut constructed of blocks of pure borax.

RITTER HOT SPRINGS

Eastern Oregon has many beautiful but seldom used highways, roads and byways. Probably only a very small percentage of people have ever traveled from Pendleton to John Day via 395. It's no freeway (thank God). It winds through rolling ranchland, dips down to several creeks and rivers, and curves through the Umatilla National Forest. From either Pendleton or John Day, Ritter is easy to find . . . just look for the middle fork of the John Day River and turn west on the road that borders it. You'll enjoy the ten mile jaunt along the quiet and relaxed Middle Fork. Then you'll see several signs, some quite picturesque, announcing the proximity of Ritter nee McDuffee Hot Spring.

We found Ritter fascinating with its old stagecoach stop hotel, general store, a number of quaint cottages, a pioneer log cabin and swinging bridge across the river. Please hurry to Ritter as the county won't allow public use of some of the old buildings because they have no foundations. It's possible by the time you are reading this they will have been replaced by a more modern but far less historically interesting restaurant. Progress ho!

We were welcomed at Ritter by Phil and Mary Trost, a couple who have owned Ritter for more than a year. It's a toss up who enjoys it most, Phil and Mary or their handsome children who make it

a point to swim in the 60' by 40' pool maintained at about 85 degrees temperature the year round. Ritter represents the type of hot spring that is well developed, clean and inviting and yet has a homey comfortable feeling that welcomes both weary travelers and hot springs lovers alike. We had several long chats with the owners who were kind enough to tell us about the history, show us the actual springs themselves and give us some insights into what they have planned for the future. They invited us to use the pool and stay overnight, both of which were most enjoyable. Phil, an expert agriculturist, has created a marvelous lawn which extends westward from the pool. Mary pointed out that in the wintertime, virtually tame deer come down to nibble the grass where the snow melts due to the hot spring water pipe buried just a few inches below the surface.

There are six trailer hookups at reasonable rates. If you like privacy, there are four baths across the swinging bridge near the springs themselves. If you don't have a trailer or camper, the several old cottages may be rented for very nominal fees by the day, week, month or, if you really dig the place enough, forever. The surrounding terrain is geologically very interesting, although somewhat sparsely floraed.

A suspension bridge leads from the Ritter Hot Springs pool area to the bathhouse containing private baths and to the source of the springs themselves. Below the bridge Ruth observes the John Day flowing gently.

Sometimes the water from a hot spring is used for irrigation or cattle watering troughs. What a waste of thermal energy.

BREITENBUSH HOT SPRINGS

A venerable old resort still operating in the traditional manner, Breitenbush offers lots of hot water (900 gallons per minute) and the kind of scenery that one expects evergreen Oregon to offer. There are a great many springs, some ranging as high as nearly 200°F.

WE DISCOVER A NEW ONE

Not listed in the government geological survey is a small but interesting springs a short distance west of Fields on the road which crosses the Steens Mountains. You won't be able to miss it because there is an oasis there . . . a variety of trees, a few buildings (decrepit) and lots of grass. There are three springs in all flowing about 50 gallons a minute at approximately 80 ft. It was obvious that they had once been partly developed for use by pioneers and, subsequently, local residents. We learned that they had been purchased—so perhaps on your visit you may find them better maintained. We hope that you'll be able to obtain permission to use them. If they have a name, let us know what it is and we'll incorporate it in the next edition of this book.

CLARENDON HOT SPRINGS

Everyone knows about Sun Valley, Idaho, the resort that the Union Pacific built and had Glenn Miller publicize in the thirties. But how many know about Clarendon Hot Springs located a few miles south of Sun Valley? We are about to correct the information gap. As you turn off the main highway, you'll have about three miles of a well-graded dirt road to travel in a westerly direction. The road is plowed in winter, so Clarendon is open all year. You won't have any difficulty locating it as it is adjacent to a small lake and is marked by a number of well-designed, rustic buildings. The hot springs facilities are well developed with many small private hot pools (private for a modest fee) plus a large pool of eminently swimmable temperature—between 80 and 90 degrees most of the time.

An old log cabin is the store and office for Clarendon.

The private pools interested us because they are thoroughly unique in this day and age of letting it all hang out. They are perhaps fifteen feet long and twelve feet wide, completely surrounded by thick rough board walls, but unroofed. Clarendon also has a nice free-and-easy policy of allowing groups to use the facilities after 10:30 p.m. Nor does one encounter the usual forbidding "No Drinking", "No eating", "No cut-offs May Be Worn in the Pool" type of signs. Frank Zoll, one of the owners, lives on the premises with his family. "Indians were the first to enjoy the springs," said Frank. "Then about 1900, weary miners came to refresh their toil-worn muscles." Frank told us that the flow rate varies between 80 and 100 gallons per minute with an average temperature of 128°F. There is another source, a pumped well, with a temperature of 133°F. So there's no lack of fresh, hot water to keep the various pools brimming full.

Of interest to readers with trailers, there are several trailer spaces for about $50 a month which includes all utilities.

Wow! This sure beats taking a bath at home. One of the two private pools (you rent them by the hour) at Clarendon.

WARSWICK HOT SPRINGS

While we were enjoying a week-long stay in Sun Valley, we examined our hot spring map for springs nearby. A large one, Warswick, or as listed in the Geologic Survey book, Wasewick, attracted us because of its 250 gallon per minute flow. Any time a spring gushes forth five, fifty-gallon drums of 150⁰F water in one minute, it must be worth seeing. And it was.

The drive westward from Sun Valley wound along a gorgeous small river, finally left it to ascend a steep mountain pass via a series of switchbacks. An old map said that we would encounter a formerly prosperous community of Carrietown, but diligent search revealed not a single trace. But a few miles farther on from the former site of this mining-lumbering community, we saw to our right the unmistakable indications of a hot spring . . . wisps of steam rising from the almost boiling flow.

Warswick is actually a complex of about fifty springs—some small, some large. The cumulative flow is what produces the extremely large volume of hot water. We ran thither and yon sticking fingers and toes into various flows. At one or two places were the remnants of attempts to create bathing pools. But since Warswick is in a shallow canyon, winter rains soon dispose of such puny efforts.

Warswick is, to our understanding, available for long-term lease and development through the Bureau of Land Management, a department of the USDA. As we explored, we visualized what an intelligent, long-range program of development could do for this primitive and now unusable area. Simple cabins, space for visitors and perhaps a series of natural stone pools would really be all that is needed to make Warswick a comfortable recreational spa.

Shirlee Van Hook says "Hot water feels pretty good on my tired feet. Wish it were deep enough—I'd take a bath."

38

Family enjoys bone warming soak in 110⁰ hot mineral water pool at Lava Hot Springs, Idaho. Water is crystal clear and odor free.

LAVA HOT SPRINGS

A bone-warming hour in Lava's 110⁰ mineral water is the perfect aprés ski. You'll sleep like a baby. A few hours from Sun Valley, Lava Hot Springs has a series of 50,000,000-year-old odor free mineral pools. Some are whirlpool equipped to tickle your ribs. It's one of the country's most highly developed natural hot water facilities, with an 86⁰ swimming pool holding nearly a million gallons of pure pleasure.

We found the Russian John Guard Station vacant so we spent some time wandering about the lovely grounds. In August wildflowers still abound in the grassy meadows. It's lush here because channels of the hot springs run in several directions through the meadow.

RUSSIAN JOHN HOT SPRINGS

Central Idaho appears to have been hit with buckshot that produced close patterns of hot springs. Many of them are centered around the fabulous resort city of Sun Valley and Elkhorn. Eighteen miles northwest, for example, you'll find Russian John, a fifty-gallon per minute 102^0F spring. It gushes forth in a meadow on the grounds of a ranger station. While we were there, we found no trace of rangers so we enjoyed exploring and photographing the as-yet unswimmable spring. It bubbles forth from a series of four sources creating shallow pools, the outlets of which merge to create a lukewarm creek.

Again, there's a great opportunity here for someone to lease and develop a valuable natural resource now going almost entirely to waste. Nearby is a beautiful creek and surrounding the region are the fabulous jagged peaks of the Sawtooth Mountains. Furthermore, Russian John is on the highway between Sun Valley and Stanley; it is our understanding that the road is snowplowed in winter which would make the springs usable the year around.

LEON'S HOT SPRINGS

Known in the U.S. Geological Survey Book as Idaho number 94, this hot spring is of far greater interest to a geologist than it would be to any bather. It is located on highway 93 between Stanley and Sunbeam. You won't have any difficulty at all finding it no matter which direction you're traveling or what the weather. It is on the north side immediately adjacent to the road. And when we say "immediately adjacent", we mean that if you turned your car off onto the shoulder, you'd give your tires a scalding hot bath. When the weather is cool, the moisture condenses rapidly and gives the entire springs area a boiler room look.

Both times that we visited this spring we were saddened by the tremendous waste of all that beautiful hot water . . . some 400 gallons per minute at a temperature in excess of 180^0F. Our thoughts envisioned a simple collecting pool for the water, either at the roadside or just below the spring on the opposite side of the road where the chilly Salmon River flows. The river could be tapped to temper the super hot water and create perhaps a series of natural rock pools, each with a different temperature.

But these musings very probably relate to some future time . . . an era when Consciousness III forest rangers give a high priority to the development of the more human natural resources in the scenic and challenging terrain that is Idaho.

For the present, the visitor must be satisfied with poking about this spectacular spring, dipping a careful finger into its near-scalding water and perhaps using the handy hose to give one's car its first and only hot bath. You might also want to run some water into a container and sample its flavor and health benefits after it has cooled down. Another activity would be to find a comfortable place to sit and imagine Indians and pioneers stopping at this granitic outcropping to ease their weary bones with the water that issues from the five separate springs.

CHALLIS HOT SPRINGS

People with families will love Challis Hot Springs located about ten miles southeast of Challis. This is a typical and well developed resort—tidy, clean, plenty of bathhouse space and a large almost olympic-size pool with a natural smooth pebble bottom. On the north side a large pipe gushes the 100-degree water which flows fast enough to change the water completely in 13 hours.

If it's raining or chilly while you're there, try the smaller indoor pool which is somewhat hotter but roomy and with the same natural stone bottom. Surrounding the developed pools are flows of hot water and a large but shallow outdoor pool that is nice to look at but unsuitable for swimming.

There are the usual amenities of an older resort . . . rooms and light meals. For a small charge you may use the picnic and camping grounds on the Salmon River. Not far away is an airstrip. Altogether, a good place to relax and enjoy the results of someone else's labors to make natural warm water highly usable.

ROBINSON BAR RANCH HOT SPRING

Carlos Casteneda, in his revelatory writings about his friend Don Juan, the Yaqui Indian, mentions the existence of a "power place". A power place might be a remote hilltop for one person or a favorite bench in a city park for another. The definition seems to be that a power place is any location on earth where you personally feel at your best. Such a place for me is Robinson Bar. It is the type of hot springs resort that a Hollywood set designer would create if he wanted to gather all of the idyllic elements that make up a place of great appeal. At Robinson Bar the delightful hot spring that gurgles out of the hillside above the ranch is almost secondary. For example, there's a charming old lodge building that once served as a stagecoach stop. It is built near the confluence of Warm Spring Creek and (for this area) the ubiquitous Salmon River. Behind the lodge are a number of rustic cabins and a couple of newer buildings, fortunately constructed within the design parameters of what is customarily accepted as Western architecture. Adjacent to the cabins are some equally picturesque corrals enclosing a number of gentle saddle horses. On the opposite side is the excellent trout fishing stream, Warm Springs Creek, which flows right through the ranch.

Exploring this ranch is a delight. On our last visit we discovered one of those beautiful old Pelton waterwheels that once provided rotary power for western pioneers. The owner and I had a discussion of how it might turn once again to generate electric power if the supply of water could be directed back to the water wheel nozzle.

Surrounding the ranch are peaks of the magnificent Sawtooths festooned with various evergreen species. Perhaps after wandering the grounds for a spell, you will encounter the two hot pools almost as an afterthought. The one adjacent to the bathhouse is large—a generous swimming pool size with water maintained in the high seventies.

Immediately above this pool is another, more intimate size bath, perhaps 10 by 14, that is maintained at about 105 degrees. This pool is the natural gathering place for guests of the ranch. We spent almost an entire afternoon there rapping with some eastern seaboard guests.

One of the friendliest couples that we met at any hot springs, Bonnie and Joe Leonard are the managers of the Robinson Bar Ranch. For them, it is a life's ambition and secret fantasy come true. They live here all year around with their children, enjoying the challenges of many types of guests and the changes of climate which, for Idaho, are not too extreme. Translated, this means that the temperature probably only goes down to 20 or 30 below zero. Joe told us that when you emerge from the hot pool on a very cold day, you'll feel warm but your wet hair will freeze!

The resort operates all year around on the American plan and if your finances permit, try it for a week or more. In summer the owners provide horses for pack trips into the White Cloud Mountain Range. In winter visitors might want to take a two or three day cross country ski trip to a cabin at Castle Peak. Or if that is too formidable, try rides in the horse drawn sleigh that brings in guests from the main highway in winter.

We could go on a long time . . . perhaps even a whole chapter about mystical magical power place Robinson Bar. We could mention the kayaking or float trips down the nearby Salmon, placer mining for gold in the area or visits to the ghost town of Custer or the silver mine at Clayton—both within easy driving distance.

Send for a brochure, in any event. It, like the place itself, is exceptionally beautiful. The address is Robinson Bar Ranch, Clayton, Idaho 83227. To reach Robinson by car, drive a short distance east beyond Sunbeam and look for the sign and the bridge that crosses the Salmon River. The resort is a mile or so along the south bank of the Salmon.

Bonnie and Joe Leonard are two people who "have it made". They manage and live at Robinson Bar Hot Springs Ranch all year round.

Three smiling bathers reflect the beneficence of Robinson Bar's hotter pool. The main pool is about twenty degrees cooler than this one which averages 105 degrees.

It's possible that the pool was once completely roofed over. But it seems more likely from the decayed top logs, that the owners merely intended to shield swimmers from vagrant breezes.

SULLIVAN HOT SPRINGS

If you follow the Salmon River a few miles east toward Clayton, you will encounter a fading sign upon which "Sullivan Hot Springs" is just barely legible. If you miss it, just beyond is a small road sign identifying Sullivan Creek. Turn in the driveway by the old sign and pass two or three cabins on your way to the careworn two-story house which has sheltered the Sullivan family for three generations. The present owner lives alone there and works in the silver mine at nearby Clayton. He has generously allowed neighbors and occasional strays like us to make use of the hot springs which are situated about 100 yards above the house, but he does appreciate a small donation in the box tacked to the front porch. We were happy to do anything to perpetuate the existence of what proved to be one of the most perfect little private natural pools we had yet come across.

Completely enclosed by wood fencing on three sides and several little dressing rooms on the fourth, you have a feeling of coziness and privacy the instant you step inside. With or without a suit, you can ease into the 105 to 110 degree water and utterly abandon yourself to relaxation. The

water is a lovely blue-grey color with natural surroundings. Bubbles rising from the smooth gravel bottom indicate where the springs are located. With a flow rate of 50 gallons per minute, the water is constantly flowing out as it is being replaced, thus providing a clarity and cleanness which are reassuring. Just above the pool is the small family cemetery where dates on the tombstones go back 100 years.

RIGGINS HOT SPRINGS

Spectacular is a good adjective to apply to this reasonably accessible resort. That's because of the geology of the Salmon River Canyon as it approaches the quaint and picturesque town of Riggins, Idaho. It's your starting point for the drive alongside the Salmon to Riggins. As you travel the well-graded road, you'll enjoy an almost continuous view of the broad, now rough now calm Salmon. You'll cross the river a total of three times and the last one, a miniature model of the Golden Gate, should turn you on. It's just about as wide as a pickup truck, so if you're traveling in anything with greater width, we suggest you park and walk in.

Chuck Wunsch and his wife are the new owners of Riggins and are working diligently to restore this once popular hot springs resort to its former beauty, charm and comfort. As we were visiting in the fall of 1973, the rustic-looking lodge was near completion. The fine pool containing the 108 degree water is surrounded by dressing rooms and sauna baths. The entire facility is in a jewel-like setting with views of the surrounding mountains, the Salmon River and a lush meadow area which surrounds the boggy terrain.

The new lodge and refurbished pool at Riggins. Eventually, the owners will create a lake for mud baths. What a place to bring up young children. Don't worry, they know how to swim.

A little stream of hot water wends its way to the Salmon Hot Springs property. The rough cabin in the back has a modern interior. The floor is heated by hot water flowing through pipes embedded in the slab.

A group of happy hotspringers wait for the pool to fill at Salmon Hot Springs. The good wine flows in the interim.

SALMON HOT SPRINGS

What happens to a hot springs that was once a reasonably well-frequented resort? Well, for one thing, people who have always wanted to own a hot springs save up their money and buy them.

Salmon has a faded elegance that we found embellished by the graciousness of the new owners, an attorney and his wife, who live in another part of Idaho. With the usual luck of a hot springs hunter, we arrived there on the very day that the owners were making one of their own infrequent visits. They were intrigued by the idea of having the hot springs mentioned in a new book, furnished us with libations and encouraged us to try the olympic-size pool. The pool has a semi-outdoor setting . . . it is roofed over, but two walls are open though protected from insects by screening. We found the water "just right," and joined several other guests in splashing and ruminations. We also toured the old hotel which is still livable and may be in the process of restoration as you read these words.

Above the lodge are several old buildings—in fact, it's almost like a small village. Step carefully and lively because hot water emerges from the ground in a number of unexpected places. A previous owner of the springs made use of some of the flow by piping it through the concrete slab floor of a small but comfortable home.

The facility abounds with opportunities and one wonders what a resurrection of interest in hot springs resorts could do for Salmon. After all, there is an airstrip nearby and the busy sports-oriented community of Salmon is only seven miles away by dirt and paved road.

When you visit Salmon, check in with the caretaker or make inquiry from local ranchers before use—that's always polite anyway—to find out if you're welcome before using any privately owned hot spring. But we're sure that if anyone's there who has the warm and outgoing personality of the present owners, you'll be as well received as we were.

SPENCER HOT SPRINGS

Few people travel Route 50 which traverses central Nevada from Reno on the west to Ely on the east. There are many reasons for this: it's a long and lonely highway with many stretches of a hundred miles or more without a single habitation, much less a service station or garage. In the summer it can be brutally hot—at other times of the year, strong desert winds blow sharp sand particles to etch windshields and take the paint off even new Cadillacs.

There's a far more popular route, 40-95, that goes from Reno through Elko and is a freeway all the way. A southern route (15) traverses the sin and sunshine capital, Las Vegas. So with these more desirable routes, you will find little traffic on 50. You'll find even less traffic when you take an unpaved road at the junction of 50 and 8A about 12 miles east of Austin, Nevada. At its inception, it appears to stretch for miles across the valley floor and finally, twisting its tail like a bewitched dragon, it disappears into the little known and mysterious Toquima Range.

About halfway after you embark on this dirt road adventure and reach the foothills of the 10,-000-foot Toquimas, you'll see a sign to your left that states Spencer Hot Springs. No mileage is given nor, for that matter, is there any other information to persuade or dissuade a hot springs afficionado. This side road appears even more deserted and chuck-hole filled than its parent, but for the intrepid thermal bath lover, the road is like a friendly invitation. It climbs very gently at the end to the very beginnings of the Toquima foothills. Even after you park at the end of the road, you won't see a single inducement to stay more than ten seconds. Sure there's a low hill, some old willow stumps supporting a weird roof, and off in the distance some corrugated sheet iron and board and batt shacks. Thus, a most pleasant and rewarding surprise greets the dusty traveler—a large if somewhat crude swimming pool filled with mineral waters that soothe both body and soul. There's even a picnic bench, not to mention a well-airconditioned bath house (the warm desert air flows easily through the cracks).

You will probably find the pool without guests, which, if you are like many hot springs lovers, suits you to a proverbial T. Occasionally, on weekends, a few people from Austin might come down for a quick dip. But tourists are even scarcer. We didn't see a single one during our own four-day stay at Spencer.

Because of the partly civilized amenities . . . concrete walkways, a valve to adjust the temperature, clean algae-free water and the bath house, it's an ideal place for novice hot springers. You don't have to do battle with crystallized minerals that cut your feet, snakes that slither from nearby bushes or the lack of a private place to change clothes. The solitary picnic bench adds to the feeling of luxury by providing a place for all three outdoor meals if you wish. With or without these gracious touches, the view down to the southernmost parts of the great Smoky Valley would be reward enough to compensate you for your trip. To have all of this and a 20 by 30 pool of warm water ranks Spencer as one of the best thermal springs that we have ever encountered.

The water in the pool contains an assortment of interesting minerals which early pioneers believed to be beneficial for arthritis and related ailments. The water emerges from several springs at temperatures ranging from 117 to 144^{0}F. The spring that supplies the pool is at the lower figure since you can almost stand being near the input valve opening. You can close the valve to lower the overall temperature of the pool if you desire. Conversely, you can plug the output and raise it a few degrees. It is suggested that you uncover the outlet before you leave so that the water can overflow through a pipe rather than off the edge of the pool which may erode the ground on the west side.

This is the type of hot spring that tempts you to stay for as long as your weary bones and your tired spirit require the reinforcement and therapy of natural warm water. There is a large parking area so plenty of room for your big trailer. Also,

the water when cooled, is deliciously drinkable. So with a plentiful supply of food, you could stay indefinitely.

One of the interesting side trips within walking distance of Spencer's is to a cluster of old miner's shacks below what was once an obviously active mining property. These shacks are evidently used by itinerants on occasion—one of them contain a cookstove, table and bed. The other boasts an old-fashioned enamel bathtub into which is piped water at a temperature higher than we cared to try. Just think . . . while you're reading these words, all that beautiful hot water is flowing in and out of that funky tub. You owe it to yourself to add a little cold water and take just one luxurious bath that will probably turn you on more than any two dozen others you've ever taken.

Closer to the Spencer Hot Spring pool are some interesting relics of perhaps six or even eight decades ago. These are large wooden troughs which were undoubtedly used by miners and desert rats

These shacks date back to an era when a nearby mine was active. At right is the outlet pipe of the bathtub. Note that the mineral-rich waters maintain a thick growth of desert grass.

to ease their aching muscles. One has a crude roof to shelter the bather from the intense Nevada sun. are so plenty of room for your big trailer. Also, many people would refer to as a "power place." We often think of the long leisurely, clothes-free swims that we enjoyed in its multi-temperature water. We think, too, of an evening when we were caught a couple of miles away by a violent electrical storm wherein noisy bolts of lightning were hurled to the desert floor only a few hundred yards from where we cowered like the young people in the classic, camp painting *The Storm*. Remembered also are the early evening sights, sounds and smells . . . eighty-mile views of untroubled desert; a distant rustle of sage brush touched by warm breezes and the smell of desert plants—a scent that defies description.

So once, before these waters run cold, enjoy them.

Your choice, arsenic or soda water. They are both free at Ojo Caliente. A little Cutty Sark added to the later improved its flavor.

ROGERS HOT SPRINGS

Assume that the world, yea, even the great universe itself, does not exist. Nothing but void. Someone, somewhere decides that what is needed is a hot springs that has everything. Rugged mountains as a backdrop, a view of cerulean blue waters —in the distance, beige sand studded with olive brush and, as the main attraction, two shimmering pools of just-right water graced by lace-like tamarisks.

Why is Rogers even more than just a hot spring? Is it because water of any kind is a novelty in desert regions? Is it just the blending of craggy cliffs with soft, warm, swimmable water? Yes, it's all of this and much much more—an ineffable *feeling* that emerges to substantiate the suspicion that all of this was planned!

No accident that the water is perfect for a desert climate—not too hot. No mischance that the bottom of the pool is smooth pebbles or that the trees filter the hot sun in the cooler parts of the water. Come and see for yourself. It's only an hour or so out of Sin City (Las Vegas) and near the shores of Lake Mead. Two pools, one deep enough for gentle paddling, several fire pits, restrooms, covered picnic tables, hiking trails all about, a natural cave with a grand view and plenty of parking for camper, trailer or your desert canary. No overnight camping at Rogers but you'll find plenty of places nearby to park your rig.

If you have some time to explore a bit, drive north from Rogers and look for a small grove of palms. These mark another similar hot springs that was once a tropical fish breeding facility. Nothing remains but a few shallow, cement-lined pools. However, the water that courses down a narrow channel is quite warm and plentiful and there's always the possibility of leasing it from the USDA or whoever has local control. Check it out; won't cost anything and it could become another Rogers.

Ojo Caliente hot springs are a popular resort in northern New Mexico. Natural mineral springs furnish the main attraction. There are separate baths and a swimming pool.

NEW MEXICO

OJO CALIENTE

Believed to be the oldest developed hot springs in North America, this relaxed facility is host to a large number of steady customers. The waters are considered to be beneficial for many human ailments. While there we observed a considerable number of people "taking the cure." There is a large outdoor pool as well as a unique indoor grotto featuring the sight of water emerging from its source . . . a fissure in a sandstone boulder. There are complete hotel and cabin facilities including a restaurant and grocery store. Ojo is adjacent to a small Mexican village and a park alongside a small river which give it a completeness not often found at a hot springs.

JEMEZ HOT SPRINGS

Just north of a typically quiet New Mexican town is this peaceful resort. Fully developed with baths and a pool, there is a modest fee to use them. Nearby is a grocery store with friendly people. It's no Warners or Murietta, but then you don't go down the byways of the Land of Enchantment for that purpose.

SPENCE HOT SPRINGS

No more than seven miles north of Jemez is another thermal spring—this one, the antithesis of Jemez. It's virtually undeveloped, merely a two-foot deep, rock-lined pool with some 100 degrees of water cascading gently therein. There's no charge other than the indeterminate price of an exciting hike down into a small-creek canyon and back up the other side.

The springs has a history of uptights vs. hang-loosers, but don't let that deter you. There probably won't be any clothes on the beautiful young people basking in the clear farm water and they probably won't mind if you make it a free hot spring too.

After you've enjoyed your soak, drift on down below the pool and enjoy the microcosmic waterfalls; each one slightly cooler than the last.

Natives informed us that Spence is especially delightful in the winter, but that it's quite a feat to ford the swollen creek. There's a log bridge up a half-mile or so that might be advisable. There is adequate parking just off the highway, but overnight camping is verboten.

OWN YOUR OWN

Renewed interest in a more natural way of life has created new enthusiasm for hot springs. An increasing number of people are examining hot springs property with the intent of ownership. As you may recall, Ritter and Sullivan hot springs in Oregon and Idaho, respectively, are owned by families that purchased them as homes, with a de-emphasis on the business aspects.

A hot spring can be an ideal place to rear a family, form a commune, establish an agricultural enterprise, or simply live in the best sense of the word. Fortunately, there are a fair number of hot springs available and probably many more if the matter were pursued with diligence. Here are two typical examples:

ORR'S HOT SPRING

Drive to Ukiah and turn east just beyond the freeway interchange and you'll find a delightful road that eventually meets the sea at Mendocino. Approximately halfway between Ukiah and the village of Comptche, you'll pass the venerable and relaxed resort of Orr's Hot Springs. A weathered bridge crosses the creek; trees of many species festoon the picturesque setting. Almost hidden are a group of buildings that resemble a sleepy Western town.

This resort has been in operation for many decades and was once a fashionable vacation place. In operation only during the summer, it needs the touch of an enthusiastic new owner-manager. The bathhouses, swimming pool, main lodge and restaurant, cabins and all equipment plus 10 acres are up for sale for about $100,000. Visualize this scenic spa as a club for health lovers or perhaps a rehabilitation facility for those who could benefit from fresh air, hot baths and a close association with nature.

MEDICAL SPRINGS

Located about 20 miles north-northeast of Baker, Oregon, this inactive resort also waits for a new awakening and intelligent direction. Once the great dream of an early Oregon pioneer, Medical Springs never reached even a small degree of its anticipated popularity. A hotel was built and a townsite platted, but the railroads ignored the area and its distance from any busy thorofare doomed Medical Springs from the start. Despite the reputed medicinal powers of the waters, no significant numbers of health-seekers ever converged on Medical Springs. It was, in terms of the English poet, a "flower born to blush unseen."

Despite this inauspicious history, there is a serene charm about the springs that invites the deft touch of a person who could appreciate the soft warm waters and transmit this appreciation to others. It will never be a Warner's or Murietta, but surely, as the planet slowly heals itself, lovers of hot springs would find their way to Medical Springs.

At present there is only a store and postoffice and the rather forlorn but neatly maintained pool, totally unused. Could it be purchased or leased? Possibly. Take the time to drive there when you're in the vicinity . . . it could be the beginning of an interesting relationship.

In another part of the book, there is a mention of Kelly's in northeast California and Warswick's in central Idaho. Both of these springs are available to purchasers or developers.

Beyond these four springs there are, no doubt, hundreds of others that could be acquired. Many hot springs now functioning might be available. After all, there is an old truism, that anything is for sale at the right price.

So if your dream is to own your own, find a hot springs in an area that appeals to you and take it from there.

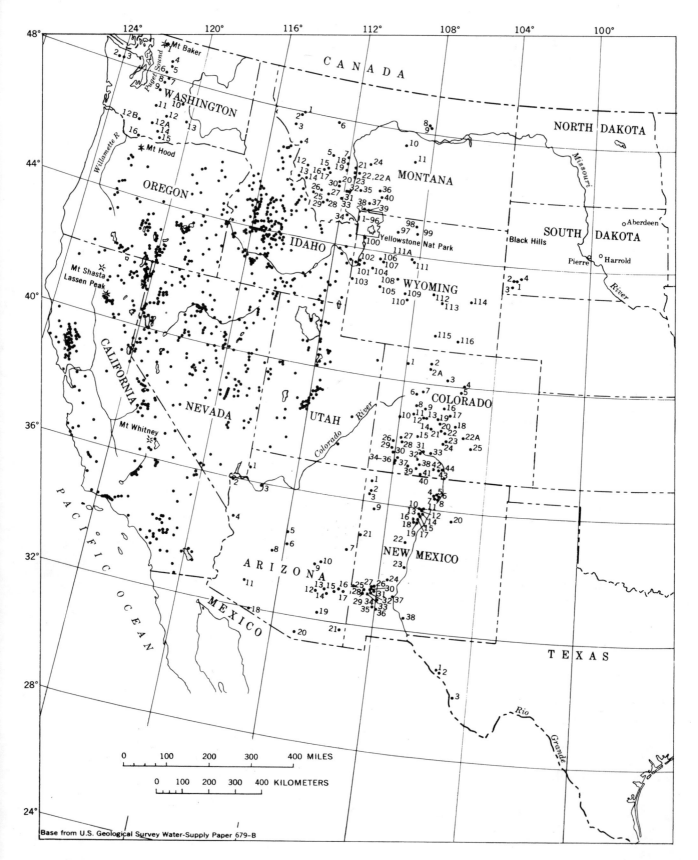

THE DIRECTORY

Each spring is listed by a figure number, its name, if any, a geographic location, the temperature of the water, flowrate in gallons per minute, the associated rocks, and remarks including use of the water.

To find a particular spring, first check the map of the state and locate its figure number. Next, refer to the state in the Directory pages and locate the corresponding figure number.

When a spring is located by its section numbers, see the county recorder's office in the respective county. They will have maps showing all the section numbers and probably additional information. Another easy method of locating a spring is to drive to the general area and ask the local folk where they go for a hot water swim.

Three states, California, Nevada, and Idaho, have nearly 200 hot springs each. Of the 140 springs listed in Wyoming, all but 21 are in Yellowstone Park. Oregon has 126 thermal springs and there are several dozen in each of the states of Colorado, Montana, New Mexico, and Utah. Arizona has 21, Texas 3. As one travels eastward, the number of springs diminishes, and we find that many states such as Florida, New York, and Pennsylvania have only one. Others have none and we sympathize with them for this lack..

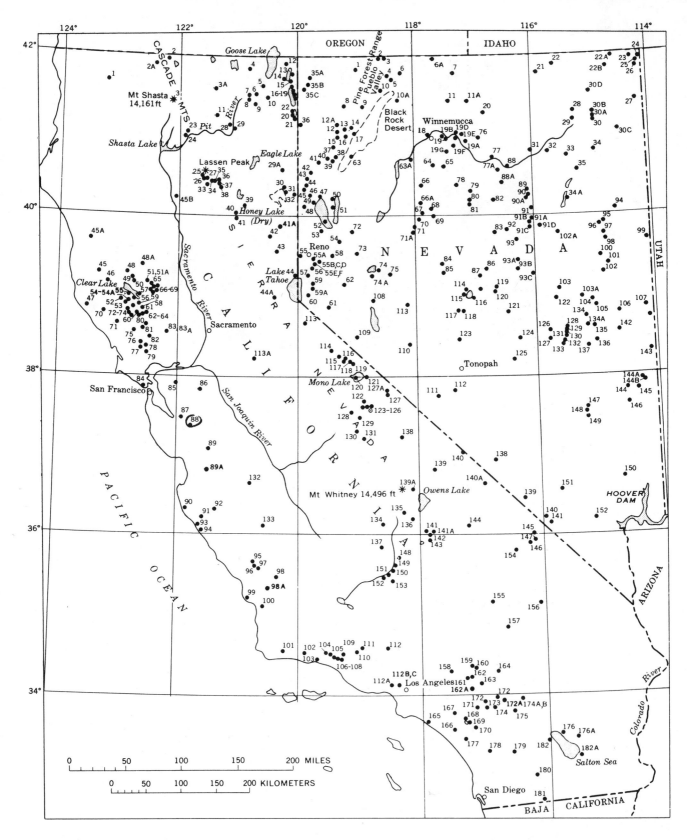

THERMAL SPRINGS OF CALIFORNIA AND NEVADA

No. on figure	Name or location	Temperature of water (°F)	Flow (gallons per minute)	Associated rocks	References on chemical quality	Remarks and additional references
				California		
1	Sec. 29, T. 15 N., R. 8 E., 14 miles southeast of Happy Camp.	90	2	Granite		Water used for bathing.
2	Klamath Hot Springs (Shovel Creek Springs), 20 miles northeast of Ager.	100–152	25	Faulted lava (Pliocene)	297	7 springs. Resort. Ref. 284.
2A	4.5 miles northeast of Ager	65–75	6	Lava overlying Cretaceous strata.		Deposit of tufa. Water supply for cattle.
3	Near top of Mount Shasta, 11 miles northeast of Sisson.	150	5	Lava (Tertiary)		2 springs. Ref. 306.
3A	North of Big Glass Mountain	191		Altered volcanic ash		Vapor vents. Ref. 302.
4	Pothole Spring, 35 miles northwest of Alturas.	70	10	Lava (Tertiary)		Ref. 297.
5	Near Rattlesnake Creek, 9 miles west to Alturas.	80	10	----do----		Do.
6	Essex Springs, in sec. 10, T. 42 N., R. 11 E.	80–92	700	----do----		5 springs. Water used for bathing and irrigation. Ref. 297.
7	Warm Spring Valley, 15 miles west of Alturas.	81	275	----do----	297	Water used for domestic supply and irrigation.
8	Kelly's Hot Spring, in sec. 29, T. 42 N., R. 10 E., 4 miles northeast of Canby.	204	325	Alluvium near faulted lava		Water used for domestic supply and irrigation. Ref. 297.
9	Near Canyon Creek, 15 miles southwest of Alturas.	80	100	Faulted(?) lava		Do.
10	1.5 miles southeast of Alturas	72	1	Alluvium overlying lava		Water supply for cattle. Ref. 297.
11	Little Hot Spring Valley, 25 miles northwest of Bieber.	127; 170	225	Basalt		2 springs. Water used for irrigation. Ref. 297.
12	Near Bidwell Creek, 1 mile northwest of Fort Bidwell.	97–108	75	Faulted lava		5 springs. Water used for domestic supply, bathing, and irrigation. Ref. 297.
13	Boyd Spring, on east side of Upper Lake, 12 miles southeast of Fort Bidwell.	70	1,000	Alluvium		Water used for irrigation.
14	Near southwest side of Upper Lake, 4 miles north of Lake City.	120–207	100	----do----		Several springs at site of spectacular mud eruption in March 1951. Refs. 264, 265, 279, 293, 297, 304.
15	Near south end of Upper Lake, 12 miles northeast of Cedarville.	170–182	80	Faulted Cretaceous strata near andesite dike.		4 springs. Water used for sheep dipping. Ref. 297.
16	Sec. 12, T. 43 N., R. 18 E., near north end of Middle Lake, 12 miles northeast of Cedarville.	140–149	225	Alluvium near faulted lava		3 springs. Water used for irrigation. Ref. 297.
17	Leonard Springs, in sec. 7, T. 43 N., R. 17 E., 11 miles northeast of Cedarville.	150	50	----do----		3 springs. Water used locally.
18	Sec. 1, T. 42 N., R. 16 E., and sec. 6, T. 42 N., R. 17 E., 5 miles east-northeast of Cedarville.	130	500	----do----		5 main springs. Water used for bathing.
18A	Cedar Plunge, 5 miles northeast of Cedarville.	180; 208	115	----do----		2 wells. Water used for bathing. Ref. 302.
19	Benmac Hot Springs, in sec. 18, T. 42 N., R. 17 E., 5 miles east of Cedarville.	120	200	----do----		Water used for irrigation. Ref. 297.
20	Menlo Warm Springs, in sec. 9, T. 39 N., R. 17 E., 5 miles south-southeast of Eagleville.	117–125	425	----do----		5 springs. Water used for bathing and irrigation. Refs. 283, 297.
21	Near southwest side of Lower Lake, 8 miles south-southeast of Eagleville.	120	100	Faulted lava		Water used for irrigation. Refs. 283, 297.
22	Bare Ranch, 12 miles south-southeast of Eagleville.	70	5	Alluvium		Refs. 283, 297.
23	Kosk Creek, 65 miles northeast of Redding	100	5	Porphyritic quartz diorite dike in sedimentary strata.		2 springs. Ref. 297.
24	Big Bend Hot Springs, in sec. 36, T. 37 N., R. 1 W.	100–180	90	----do----		6 springs. Resort. Ref. 297.
25	Upper Mill Creek, 1 mile northwest of Tophet Hot Springs (No. 26).	120–150	3	Lava (Tertiary)		3 springs. Refs. 239, 307.
26	Tophet (Soupan, Supan) Hot Springs, on southwest side of Lassen Peak, 53 miles northeast of Red Bluff.	175 to boiling	5	----do----		About 10 springs and mud pots. Deposits of sulfur. Refs. 213, 238, 239, 297, 307, 660.
27	Bumpas Hot Springs, on south side of Lassen Peak, 60 miles northeast of Red Bluff.	Boiling	100	----do----		About 20 springs. Refs. 213, 239, 240, 258, 297, 307, 660.
28	Bassett Hot Springs, 2.5 miles east-northeast of Bieber.	173	175	Tuffaceous sandstone (late Tertiary).	297	Water used for bathing and irrigation.
29	Stonebreaker Hot Springs, 6 miles east-southeast of Bieber.	110–165	125	----do----		9 springs. Water used for irrigation. Ref. 297.
29A	Tipton Springs	70	925	Basalt (Tertiary)		Water used for irrigation.
30	Shaffer (Branbecks) Hot Springs, near north shore of Honey Lake.	160–204	250	Faulted(?) alluvium	297	3 springs. Water used for bathing. Refs. 128, 252, 413, 441, 526.
31	Amedee Hot Springs, near Amedee railroad station.	178–204	700	----do----	297	7 springs. Water used for bathing. Refs. 125, 256, 441.
32	Highrock Spring, 10 miles east-southeast of Amedee.	86	525	Basalt (Tertiary)		Water used for domestic purposes and irrigation. Ref. 297.
33	Morgan Hot Springs, 53 miles northeast of Red Bluff.	90–200	85	----do----	297	26 springs. Campground. Refs. 239, 307.

No. on figure	Name or location	Temperature of water (°F)	Flow (gallons per minute)	Associated rocks	References on chemical quality	Remarks and additional references
34	Devil's Kitchen, 1.5 miles west of Drake Hot Springs (No. 36).	150–205	50	Basalt (Tertiary)	297	About 30 springs. Refs. 213, 239, 240, 307, 660.
35	Hot Spring Valley, 0.5 mile west of Drake Hot Springs (No. 36).	83	8	----do		Water is carbonated. Used for drinking. Ref. 297.
36	Drake Hot Springs, 6 miles southeast of Lassen Peak and 70 miles northeast of Red Bluff.	123–148	20	----do		4 springs. Resort. Ref. 239, 297.
37	Boiling Spring (Tartarus) Lake, 1 mile south of Drake Hot Springs (No. 36).	170–190	Intermittent	----do		10 springs. Refs. 213, 239, 240, 297, 307, 660.
38	Terminal Geyser, 3.5 miles southeast of Drake Hot Springs (No. 36).	120–205	8	----do		6 springs. Refs. 239, 297, 307.
39	Kruger Springs, 1 mile east of Greenville	90–106	8	Alluvium overlying faulted granite.		5 springs. Water used for bathing. Ref. 297.
40	Sec. 13, T. 25 N., R. 8 E., 2 miles northeast of Twain.	94	20	Slate (Carboniferous)		
41	Sec. 14, T. 25 N., R. 8 E., on Indian Creek, 1 mile east of Twain.	80–98	35	----do		7 springs.
41A	Marble Hot Wells, 5 miles south-southeast of Beckwourth.	125–161	350			3 wells. Water used for domestic purposes, bathing, and irrigation. Ref. 297.
42	McLear Sulphur Springs, 5 miles southwest of Beckwourth.	86	140	Lake Beds (Pleistocene)		8 springs. Water used for domestic purposes and irrigation. Refs. 292, 297.
43	Campbell (Upper Soda, Freys) Hot Springs, 2 miles south of Sierraville.	65–111	80	Faulted andesite		11 springs. Resort. Refs. 284, 297.
44	Brockway (Carnelian) Hot Springs, on north shore of Lake Tahoe and 13 miles southeast of Truckee.	120–140	150	Andesite overlying faulted granodiorite.	137	6 springs. Resort. Ref. 297.
44A	Wentworth Springs	60–75	Small	Granite-slate contact		2 groups of springs. Water is carbonated. Deposits of tufa. Campground.
45	Orrs Hot Springs, 16 miles northwest of Ukiah.	63–104	25	Franciscan Formation (Jurassic and Cretaceous).	263	7 springs. Resort. Ref. 297.
45A	0.5 mile north of Laytonville	70	200	----do		Water contains H_2S. Used for bathing.
45B	Tuscan (Lick) Springs	86	50	----do		20 springs. Water is saline, contains H_2S. Natural gas. Resort. Ref. 306.
46	Vichy Springs, 3 miles northeast of Ukiah	50–90	30	Sandstone (Franciscan Formation) near lava.	263, 284, 297	7 springs. Resort.
47	Point Arena Hot Springs, 15 miles southeast of Point Arena	110–112	4.5	Basalt (Tertiary)		2 springs. Resort. Ref. 297.
48	Crabtree Springs, 38 miles north-north-east of Lakeport	68–105	15	Sandstone (Franciscan Formation).		4 springs. Campground. Ref. 297.
48A	Fouts Springs	60–75	20	Serpentine (Franciscan Formation).		4 springs. Water is saline and carbonated. Resort.
49	Sec. 35, T. 16 N., R. 8 W., 2 miles northwest of Bartlett (cold) Springs.	90	5	----do		Water used for bathing.
50	Newman (Soap Creek) Springs, 45 miles west of Williams.	70–92	25	----do		9 springs. Water used for bathing. Ref. 297.
51	Complexion Springs, 28 miles west of Williams.	74	1	----do	297	30 springs.
51A	Chalk Mountain	67–70	3	Altered lava		3 springs. Water is saline and carbonated. Deposit of tufa.
52	Highland Springs, 6 miles southwest of Kelseyville.	52–82	20	Serpentine (Franciscan Formation).	137, 253, 297	11 springs. Resort.
53	England (Elliott) Springs, 8 miles southwest of Kelseyville.	56–76	8	Sandstone (Franciscan Formation).		7 springs. Water used for drinking. Ref. 297.
54	Carlsbad Springs, 5 miles south of Kelseyville.	66–76	4	----do	297	4 springs. Water used locally.
54A	Kelseyville	78	10			3 wells. Water used for irrigation.
55	Soda Bay Springs, at base of Mount Konocti.	80–87	400	Lava (Quaternary)	297	5 springs. Resort. Ref. 253.
56	Near southwest shore of Clear Lake, 10 miles east of Kelseyville.	70–100	5	Andesite (Tertiary)		10 springs. Water used for drinking. Ref. 297.
57	Sulphur Bank (Hot Bolata) Hot Springs, 10 miles north-northwest of Lower Lake.	83–120	----	Basalt near faulted Lower Cretaceous strata.	20, 128, 297, 306	10 springs. Deposits of cinnabar and sulfur. Refs. 214, 225, 244, 245, 252, 260, 274–277, 288, 293, 303, 400, 401, 426.
58	Howard Springs, 28 miles north-northwest of Calistoga.	48–110	135	Sandstone and serpentine (Franciscan Formation).	137, 297	26 springs. Resort. Ref. 284.
59	Seigler Springs, 30 miles north-northwest of Calistoga.	58–126	35	Serpentine (Franciscan Formation).	284, 297	13 springs. Resort. Ref. 253.
60	Gordon Hot Spring, 28 miles north-northwest of Calistoga.	92	5	Lava overlying sandstone (Franciscan Formation).	284, 297	Water used locally. Ref. 216.
61	Spiers (Copsey) Springs, 24 miles north-northwest of Calistoga.	78; 84	15	Serpentine (Franciscan Formation).		2 springs. Water is bottled for drinking. Ref. 297.
62	Castle (Mills) Hot Springs, 25 miles north-northwest of Calistoga.	65; 164	----	Schist (Franciscan Formation).	297	2 springs. Resort. Ref. 253.
63	Anderson Springs, 22 miles north-northwest of Calistoga.	63–145	7	Lava and schist (Franciscan Formation).	297	9 springs. Resort. Refs. 216, 253, 284, 286.
64	Harbin Springs, 20 miles north-northwest of Calistoga.	90–120	10	Schist (Franciscan Formation).	137, 284, 297	3 springs. Resort. Refs. 216, 253, 284.
65	Deadshot Springs, 28 miles west-southwest of Williams.	65–79	11	Serpentine (Franciscan Formation).		4 springs. Water used for drinking. Ref. 297.
66	Blancks Hot Springs, 27 miles southwest of Williams.	120	4	Sandstone (Franciscan Formation).		2 springs. Water used for bathing. Refs. 246, 297.
67	Jones Hot Springs, 26.5 miles southwest of Williams.	125	2	Serpentine (Franciscan Formation).		Well that flows intermittently. Former resort. Refs. 246, 297.
67A	Manzanita Quicksilver Mine	110–142	4	----do		3 springs. Water is saline and sulfurous. Used for bathing. Ref. 246.
68	Wilbur (Simmons) Hot Springs, 26 miles southwest of Williams.	65–140	35	Serpentine and sandstone (Franciscan Formation).	297	12 springs. Resort. Refs. 137, 246, 284.
69	Elgin Quicksilver Mine, 30 miles west-southwest of Williams.	140–153	25	----do	297	3 springs. Refs. 109, 216, 246.
70	Hoods (Fairmount) Hot Springs, 15 miles west-northwest of Cloverdale.	100	5	Fractured sedimentary strata (Franciscan Formation) near schist.	297	2 springs. Water used for bathing. Ref. 297.
71	Skagg's Hot Springs, 9 miles west-southwest of Geyserville.	120–135	15	Fractured sedimentary strata (Franciscan Formation).	266	3 springs. Resort. Refs. 284, 297.

No. on figure	Name or location	Temperature of water (°F)	Flow (gallons per minute)	Associated rocks	References on chemical quality	Remarks and additional references
72	The Geysers, 18 miles east-southeast of Cloverdale.	140 to boiling	30–50	Fractured sedimentary strata (Franciscan Formation).	137, 278, 297	About 30 springs, including Iron, Witches' Cauldron, Devil's Teakettle, and Acid. Water is bottled for drinking. Resort. Also wells produce steam for generation of electricity. Refs. 19, 75, 130, 211, 212, 220, 221, 223, 224, 226–230, 233, 237, 241, 242, 267, 284, 285, 288, 296, 306, 400.
73	Sulphur Creek, 21 miles southeast of Cloverdale.	120	5	.....do................		Several springs. Ref. 212.
74	Little Geysers, 22 miles east, southeast of Cloverdale.	110–160	8	.....do................		10 springs. Campground. Refs. 137, 212, 228, 230, 288, 297.
75	Mark West Warm Springs, 7 miles northeast of Fulton.	60–82	30	Lava and tuff (Pliocene)		9 springs. Resort. Ref. 297.
76	Los Guilicos Warm Springs, 3.5 miles southwest of Glen Ellen.	78; 82	5	Franciscan Formation		2 springs. Resort. Ref. 297.
77	McEwan Ranch, 3 miles southwest of Kenwood.	80	50	Lava and tuff (Pliocene)		Water used for irrigation. Ref. 297.
78	Eldridge State Home, 6 miles north-north-west of Sonoma.	72	10	Alluvium overlying lava		Do.
79	Ohms and Boyes Hot Springs, 2 miles northwest of Sonoma.	114–118		Lava and pre-Tertiary sedimentary strata.	297	Pumped wells at site of springs which stopped flowing in 1906. Water bottled for table use. Resort. Ref. 284.
79	Fetters Hot Springs, 2.75 miles northwest of Sonoma.	100				4 pumped wells. Resort. Refs. 284, 297.
79	Agua Caliente (Aqua Rica) Springs, 3 miles northwest of Sonoma.	97–115	10			5 flowing wells. Resort. Ref. 297.
80	Aetna Springs, 17 miles north of St. Helena.	63–92	20	Franciscan Formation	266, 297	6 springs. Water used for drinking. Resort. Refs. 216, 284, 311.
81	Calistoga Hot Springs, 225 yds. east of depot.	126–173	8	Faulted tuff (Pliocene?)	270, 297	4 springs and several flowing wells. Water used for bathing. Refs. 212, 267, 276, 284, 285.
82	St. Helena White Sulphur Springs, 2 miles southwest of St. Helena.	69–90	6	Sandstone (Franciscan Formation).	297	5 springs. Resort. Refs. 144, 216.
83	Napa Rock (Priest) Soda Springs, 15 miles east-northeast of St. Helena.	79	15	Altered sandstone and shale (Franciscan Formation).	297	2 springs. Water used for drinking. Ref. 284.
83A	Phillips Soda Springs............	68; 76	10	Serpentine (Franciscan Formation).		2 springs. Deposit of MgCO$_3$.
84	Rocky Point Spring, 6 miles northeast of Point Bonita.	100	5	Sandstone (Franciscan Formation).		Ref. 297, 299.
85	Sulphur Springs, 2 miles northeast of Walnut Creek (town).	75–81	5	Faulted sandstone (Tertiary).		6 springs. Water used for domestic purposes. Ref. 297.
86	Byron Hot Springs, 2 miles south of Byron.	72–120	15	Sedimentary strata (upper Miocene).	284, 297	7 springs. Resort. Refs. 137, 216, 253.
87	Warm Springs, 2 miles northeast of Warm Springs (town).	85–90	15	Faulted sedimentary strata (Teritary).		4 springs. Water used for domestic purposes and watering garden. Ref. 297.
88	Alum Rock Park Springs, 7 miles northwest of San Jose.	62–87	15	Folded sedimentary strata (Teritary).	297	17 springs. Water used for drinking and bathing.
89	Gilroy Hot Spring, 14 miles northeast of Gilroy.	110	15	Faulted(?) Franciscan Formation.	297	Water bottled for table use. Resort. Refs. 216, 284.
89A	San Benito Mineral Well, 4 miles southeast of Hollister.	75				Pumped well. Water bottled for table use.
90	North Fork of Little Sur River, 30 miles (by road) south of Monterey.	103; 114		Faulted granite		2 springs. Ref. 297.
91	Tassajara Hot Springs, in sec. 32, T. 19 S., R. 4 E.	100–140	100	Gneiss and granite	297	17 springs. Resort.
92	Paraiso Hot Springs, 8 miles south-south-west of Soledad.	65–111	10	Sandstone (Miocene)	270, 272, 297	5 springs. Resort. Refs. 216, 282.
93	Slate's Hot Springs, in sec. 9, T. 21 S., R. 3 E.	100–121	50	Sedimentary strata (Upper Cretaceous).		10 springs. Resort. Refs. 247, 272, 297.
94	Dolan's Hot Springs, 7 miles from Slate's Hot Springs.	100	5	.....do................		
95	Paso de Robles Mud Bath Springs, 2.5 miles north of Paso Robles.	55–118	100	Sedimentary strata (Pliocene).	297	3 springs. Water bottled for table use; also used for bathing. Ref. 216.
96	Paso de Robles Hot Springs, in southwest part of Paso Robles.	105	1,700	.....do................	270, 272, 284, 297	1 main spring and flowing well. Resort. Ref. 216.
97	Santa Ysabel Springs, 4 miles southeast of Paso Robles.	94	150	.....do................	270, 297	2 springs. Water used for bathing and irrigation.
98	Cameta Warm Spring, 30 miles southeast of Paso Robles.	74	3	Faulted gravel (Quaternary).		Water used for bathing. Ref. 297.
98A	San Luis (Sycamore) Hot Spring, 8 miles south-southwest of San Luis Obispo.	107	50			Well. Resort. Refs. 217, 284, 400.
99	Pecho Warm Springs, 15 miles southwest of San Luis Obispo.	72; 95	17	Folded shale (Miocene)		2 springs. Water used for drinking and bathing. Refs. 217, 297.
100	Newsom's Arroyo Grande Warm Springs, 2.5 miles east of Arroyo Grande.	98	15	Fractured siliceous shale (Miocene).	270, 297	Resort. Ref. 216.
101	Las Cruces Hot Springs, 4 miles north of Gaviota station.	67–97	50	Sandstone (Miocene) faulted(?) against upper Eocene strata.		4 springs. Water used for bathing. Ref. 297.
102	San Marcos (Mountain Glen, Cuyama) Hot Springs, 20 miles northwest of Santa Barbara.	89–108	45	Faulted sandstone (Miocene).		6 springs. Campground. Refs. 262, 297.
103	Montecito (Santa Barbara) Hot Springs, 6 miles northeast of Santa Barbara.	111–118	50	Sandstone (upper Eocene)	297	11 springs. Resort. Source of part of Montecito water supply. Refs. 219, 262, 306.
104	Sec. 4, T. 5 N., R. 25 W., 1 mile east of Mono Creek and 12 miles northeast of Santa Barbara.	90	15	Shale (upper Eocene)		3 springs.
105	Sec. 1, T. 5 N., R. 25 W., 4 miles north of Santa Ynez River and 15 miles northeast of Santa Barbara.	90	10	.....do................		Do.
106	Vicker's Hot Springs, in Matilija Canyon, 9 miles northwest of Nordhoff.	118	5	Faulted(?) sandstone (upper Eocene).	297	3 springs. Ref. 234.
107	Stingley's Hot Springs, 8.5 miles northwest of Nordhoff.	76; 100	4	.....do................		2 springs. Water used for domestic purposes and bathing. Ref. 297.

No. on figure	Name or location	Temperature of water (°F)	Flow (gallons per minute)	Associated rocks	References on chemical quality	Remarks and additional references
108	Matilija Hot Springs, 6 miles northwest of Nordhoff.	65–116	45	Sandstone and shale (upper Eocene).	234, 297	4 springs. Resort. Ref. 128
109	Wheeler's Hot Springs, 7.5 miles north-northwest of Nordhoff.	62–102	40	____do____	234, 297	4 springs. Resort.
110	Willett Hot Spring, in sec. 31, T. 6 N., R. 20 W., 24 miles north-northwest of Fillmore.	120	50	____do____		Water used for bathing.
111	Sespe Hot Springs, in sec. 21, T. 6 N., R. 20 W., 22 miles north-northwest of Fillmore.	97–191	125	Faulted granite		4 springs. Campground. Refs. 262, 297.
112	Elizabeth Lake Canyon, 13 miles north-northeast of Castaic station.	100	5	____do____		Ref. 297.
112A	Encino Ranch (Seminole) Hot Springs.	85	5	Shale (Miocene)	262	2 springs. Water is carbonated. Used for domestic purposes and bathing. Refs. 297, 306.
112B	Radium Sulphur Spring, in northwestern part of Los Angeles.	80				Pumped well. Water used for bathing. Ref. 297.
112C	Bimini Hot Spring, in northern part of Los Angeles.	104	100			Flowing well. Water used for bathing. Ref. 297.
113	Grover's Hot Springs, 4 miles west of Markleeville.	128–146	100	Faulted granite		12 springs. Campground. Ref. 297.
113A	Valley Springs	75	1	Miocene(?) strata near contact with Upper Jurassic strata.		2 springs. Water slightly saline. Bottled for table use.
114	Fales' Hot Springs, in sec. 24, T. 6 N., R. 23 E., 13 miles northwest of Bridgeport.	97–141	300	Lava near granite		Several springs. Deposit of tufa. Resort. Refs. 125, 297.
115	Buckeye Hot Spring, in sec. 3, T. 4 N., R. 24 E., 5.5 miles west-southwest of Bridgeport.	140	25	Faulted granite		Water used for bathing. Refs. 282, 297.
116	Sec. 27, T. 5 N., R. 25 E., 1.5 miles southeast of Bridgeport.	121–148	10	Fissured andesite	297	3 main springs. Water used for bathing and sheep dipping. Quarries in onyx marble and travertine nearby. Refs. 235, 236, 251, 282, 302.
117	1.5 miles south-southeast of Bridgeport	70–105	25	____do____		20 springs. Refs. 282, 297, 305.
118	Warm Springs Flat, 5 miles southeast of Bridgeport.	100	5	Lava (Tertiary)		Water used for cattle supply. Refs. 282, 297.
119	Sec. 20, T. 4 N., R. 26 E., near Mormon Creek, 7 miles southeast of Bridgeport.	100	5	____do____		Water used for cattle supply. Ref. 297.
120	Paoha Island in Mono Lake	176	100	Lava (Recent)	409	Several springs. Refs. 275, 282, 297, 305, 306.
121	Mono Basin Warm Spring, on east edge of Mono Lake.	90	10	____do____	128, 137, 282, 297, 409.	
122	Sec. 13, T. 3 S., R. 28 E., 5 miles northeast of Casa Diablo Hot Springs (No. 123).	170	5	Faulted lava (Recent)		Refs. 282, 297.
123	Casa Diablo Hot Springs, in sec. 32, T. 3 S., R. 28 E., on U.S. Highway 395.	115–194	35	Basalt (Quaternary)		20 springs. Small deposit of sinter. Water used for vapor baths. Refs. 282, 297, 305.
124	Casa Diablo Hot Pool, in sec. 35, T. 3 S., R. 28 E., 3 miles northeast of Casa Diablo.	180	Intermittent	Faulted(?) lava (Quaternary)		Ref. 297.
125	The Geysers, in sec. 30, T. 3 S., R. 29 E.	120–202	500	Rhyolite (Quaternary)		5 main springs and 2 stream vents. Large deposit of tufa. Ref. 305.
126	Whitmore Warm Springs, in sec. 18, T. 4 S., R. 29 E.	90	306	Faulted lava (Quaternary)		2 main springs. Resort. Ref. 125.
127	Benton Hot Springs, in sec. 2, T. 2 S., R. 31 E., 300 yd northwest of Benton post office.	135	400	Granite near Tertiary volcanic tuff.		Water used for irrigation. Refs. 262, 297, 305, 310.
127A	Bertrand Ranch	70	100	Alluvium		Water used for irrigation.
128	Reds Meadows Hot Springs, 10 miles southwest of Mineral Park.	90–120	10	Granite near lava	297	5 springs. Campground.
129	Fish Creek Hot Springs, in sec. 9, T. 5 S., R. 27 E., at head of Fish Valley.	110	5	Granite		2 springs. Ref. 297.
130	Sec. 16, T. 7 S., R. 27 E., on South Fork of San Joaquin River.	100–112	25	____do____		4 springs. Campground. Ref. 297.
131	Blaney Meadows Hot Springs, in sec. 10, T. 8 S., R. 28 E.	100–110	40	Gneiss	297	8 springs. Campground.
132	Mercey Hot Springs, 25 miles south of Dos Palos.	79–109	6	Fractured greenstone near Francisian Formation.	215, 297	3 springs. Water is brackish. Used for bathing.
133	Fresno Hot Springs, on branch of Waltham Creek, 18 miles west of Coalinga.	88–97	20	Faulted sandstone and shale (Miocene?).		5 springs. Resort. Refs. 250, 297.
134	South Fork of the Middle Fork of Tule River, 27.5 miles east-northeast of Portersville.	77	25	Granite		Water is carbonated. Used for drinking. Ref. 297.
135	Jordan Hot Springs, 65 miles north of Kernville.	95–123	75	Gravel near lava		14 springs. Large deposit of tufa. Campground. Ref. 297.
136	Monache Meadows, 14 miles southwest of Olancha.	100	2	Rhyolite (Tertiary)		Water is carbonated. Used for drinking. Ref. 297.
137	California (Deer Creek) Hot Springs	105–126	50	Faulted granite		7 springs. Resort. Refs. 284, 297.
138	Keough Hot Springs, 8 miles south of Bishop.	130	825	Faulted(?) granite		3 springs. Water used for bathing. Resort. Ref. 297.
139	Saline Valley, 10 miles northeast of Saline Valley Borax Mine.	100	5	Alluvium		Ref. 297.
139A	Skinner Ranch	Warm	10	____do____		Water used for domestic purposes and irrigation.
140	Staininger Ranch (Grapevine) Springs, in Grapevine Canyon, 50 miles northeast of Keeler.	75	30	Lake beds (Tertiary)		Several springs. Water used for domestic purposes and irrigation. Refs. 297, 399.
140A	Keene Wonder Spring, at west base of Funeral Range. Nevares and Texas springs are farther south.	80–93	30	Tertiary strata overlying Paleozoic strata.		1 main and several minor springs. Water contains 3,630 ppm of dissolved solids. Extensive deposit of tufa.
141	14 miles southeast of Haiwee	150–203	Small	Lava (Tertiary)		20 pools and vapor vents. Deposits of sulfur and alum. Refs. 262, 297.
141A	Devil's Kitchen, 2 miles northeast of Coso Hot Springs (No. 142).	180 to boiling	Small	Lava (Recent)		Several small springs and vapor vents. Small deposits of cinnabar. Refs. 248, 275.
142	Coso Hot Springs, 20 miles northeast of Little Lake.	140 to boiling	Small	Lava (Recent) overlying granite.	297	3 main springs. Steam baths. Resort. Refs. 248, 252, 266, 275, 280, 308.

No. on figure	Name or location	Temperature of water (°F)	Flow (gallons per minute)	Associated rocks	References on chemical quality	Remarks and additional references
				California—Continued		
143	Near Little Lake, 18 miles south of Haiwee.	80	1	Basalt (Tertiary)	297	Ref. 262.
144	Panamint Valley, 4 miles north of Ballarat.	80	1	Alluvium near granite		Water supply for prospectors. Refs. 261, 297.
145	Yeoman Hot Springs, in sec. 1, T. 21 N., R. 7 E., 5 miles northeast of Zabriskie.	80	100	Alluvium near Tertiary lava.		Several springs. Water used for irrigation. Refs. 289, 290.
146	2 miles north of Tecopa	108; 109	225	Faulted quartzite (Cambrian).		2 springs. Water supply for railroad. Ref. 297.
147	Resting Spring, 5.5 miles northeast of Tecopa.	80	260	____do____		Water used for domestic purposes and irrigation. Ref. 297.
148	2 miles northeast of Kernville	98; 113	4	Faulted gneiss		2 springs. Water used for bathing. Refs. 262, 297.
149	Neills Hot Spring (Agua Caliente), 7 miles south-south-west of Kernville.	131	115	Faulted granite and gneiss.		Water used for domestic purposes, bathing, and irrigation. Refs. 262, 297.
150	Clear Creek (Hobo) Hot Springs, in sec. 25, T. 27 S., R. 32 E.	119	20	Granite		3 springs. Water used locally. Ref. 297.
151	Delonegha Springs, 45 miles northeast of Bakersfield.	104–112	25	Fractured granite		3 springs. Resort. Ref. 297.
152	Democrat Springs, 40 miles northeast of Bakersfield.	100–115	25	Faulted granite		5 springs. Resort. Ref. 297.
153	Williams Hot Springs, 16 miles northeast of Caliente.	60–100	20	Fractured gneiss and quartz.		5 springs. Water contains H_2S. Used for domestic purposes, bathing, and irrigation. Ref. 297.
154	Saratoga Springs, 15 miles west of Sperry railroad station.	82	125	Faulted intrusive diorite.	290	4 springs. Water supply for prospectors. Refs. 271, 289, 297.
155	Paradise Springs, 25 miles north of Daggett.	85–106.5	30	Pegmatite	290	Several springs. Water supply for prospectors. Refs. 269, 289, 297.
156	Soda Station Springs, in sec. 14, T. 12 N., R. 8 E.	75	30	Faulted(?) limestone (Precambrian).	290	2 springs. Water used for drinking.
157	Newberry Spring, in sec. 32, T. 9 N., R. 3 E., 600 yd south of Newberry railroad station.	77	300	Alluvium (Quaternary) near tuffaceous lava (Tertiary).		Pumped. Water supply for railroad. Refs. 289, 290, 297.
158	Tylers Bath Springs, in Lytle Canyon, 15 miles northwest of San Bernardino.	92	5	Granite		Refs. 262, 297.
159	Sec. 15, T. 3 N., R. 3 W., in Deep Creek Canyon, 16 miles southeast of Victorville.	80–100	5	____do____		Several small springs.
160	Sec. 14, T. 3 N., R. 3 W., in Deep Creek Canyon, 15 miles southeast of Victorville.	80–100	5	____do____		6 springs.
161	Harlem Hot Spring, 5 miles north-north-east of San Bernardino.	120				Pumped well. Water used for bathing. Refs. 268, 297.
162	Waterman Hot Springs, 6.5 miles northeast of San Bernardino.	123	5	Fractured granite and gneiss.	297	Several small springs. Water used for bathing. Refs. 262, 284.
162	Arrowhead Hot Springs, 7 miles northeast of San Bernardino.	110–187	50	____do____	137, 268, 284, 297	2 groups of springs. Resort. Ref. 262.
162A	Urbita Hot Springs, 1 mile south of San Bernardino.	80–106	250			6 wells. Water used for bathing. Refs. 268, 297.
163	Sec. 34, T. 1 N., R. 2 W., in Santa Ana Canyon, 12 miles east-northeast of San Bernardino.	90	3	Granite		
164	Near Baldwin Lake, 40 miles southeast of Victorville.	88	5	____do____		Water used for bathing. Ref. 297.
165	Fairview Hot Spring, 7 miles southwest of Santa Ana.	96	15	Alluvium		Water bottled for table use. Resort. Ref. 297.
166	San Juan Capistrano Hot Springs, 13 miles northeast of San Juan Capistrano.	121–124	35	Faulted(?) granite	297	6 springs. Visited by Francisan friars and mentioned in their records. Ref. 262.
167	Glen Ivy (Temescal) Hot Spring, 11 miles south-southeast of Corona.	102	15	Faulted granite	291, 298	1 main and several minor springs. Resort. Ref. 297.
168	Wrenden (Bundys Elsinore) Hot Springs, 225 yd north of Elsinore depot.	118		Alluvium	291, 297, 298	Originally flowed, now pumped. Resort.
169	Elsinore Hot Springs, 50 yd north of Elsinore depot.	125		Quaternary deposits near faulted Mesozoic rocks.	137, 298	3 springs which originally flowed but now are pumped. Resort. Ref. 297.
170	Murrieta Hot Springs, 4 miles east-north-east of Murrieta.	134–136	75	Faulted granite	284, 291, 297, 298	3 springs. Resort.
171	Pilares Hot Spring, 8 miles northeast of Perris.	100	3	Alluvium overlying faulted bedrock.	298	Water used for bathing. Also drilled well nearby. Ref. 297.
172	Eden Hot Springs, 9 miles southwest of Beaumont.	90–110	30	Faulted granite	291, 298	8 springs. Resort. Refs. 268, 297.
172A	Highland Springs	112 (max)		Granite near San Andreas fault.	291	Several springs. Water used for bathing. Refs. 236, 253.
173	Gilman (San Jacinto, Relief) Hot Springs, 6 miles northwest of San Jacinto.	83–116	20	Alluvium overlying gneiss.	291, 297, 298	6 springs. Resort. Ref. 268.
174	Soboba (Ritchey) Hot Springs, 2.5 miles northeast of San Jacinto.	70–111	25	Faulted gneiss	291, 297, 298	6 springs. Water bottled for table use; also used for irrigation. Resort. Ref. 268.
174A	Desert, in sec. 30, T. 2 S., R. 5 E	112–116		Alluvium near San Andreas fault.	291	8 wells about 300 ft deep. Water used for bathing.
174B	Lucky Seven, 2 miles southeast of Desert.	200		Valley alluvium		Drilled well. Water used for bathing. Ref. 302.
175	Palm Springs, 6 miles south of Palm Springs station.	100	5	Faulted granite	232, 291, 297	2 springs. Resort. Refs. 231, 255, 284.
176	Dos Palmas Spring, on northeast side of Salton Sink, 6 miles east of Salton railroad station.	80	25	Alluvium overlying Tertiary strata.	232, 282, 297	Water supply for prospectors. Ref. 262.
176A	Hot Mineral Well	186	900	Alluvium near fault		300 ft deep. Water used for bathing. Refs. 249, 302.
177	Deluz Warm Springs, 20 miles north-northeast of Oceanside.	84–88	5	Diorite dike in granite		3 springs. Water used locally. Refs. 262, 297.
178	Agua Tibia Spring, 30 miles northeast of Oceanside.	92	10	Faulted granite	297	Water used for bathing and irrigation.
179	Warner (Las Aguas Calientes) Hot Springs, in sec. 36, T. 10 S., R. 3 E.	131–139	150	____do____	137, 232, 297	6 springs. Water used for irrigation. Resort. Ref. 218, 222, 243, 255, 287, 784.
180	Agua Caliente Springs, in secs. 18 and 19, T. 14 S., R. 7 E.	90	20	____do____		Several springs. Campground. Refs. 232, 269, 297.

No. on figure	Name or location	Temperature of water (°F)	Flow (gallons per minute)	Associated rocks	References on chemical quality	Remarks and additional references
	California—Continued					
181	Jacumba Springs, in secs. 7 and 8, T. 18 S., R. 8 E.	94; 96	15	Fractured granite		2 springs. Water used for bathing and irrigation. Refs. 232, 297.
182	Fish Springs, on west side of Salton Sea, 13 miles south of Mecca.	90	280	Alluvium	232	Several springs, also wells 260–850 ft deep. Water supply for prospectors. Refs. 269, 297.
182A	Salton volcanoes	100 to boiling	Small	Alluvium near fault		4 main groups on southeast-northwest line 2.5 miles long. Refs. 249, 254, 255, 257, 259, 270, 294, 300, 304, 746.

INTERESTING FACT: Just above San Bernardino, Ca. there's a scalding spring that issues from a fractured granite mass. It's called Arrowhead Hot Springs and has a temperature of 180 F. It's commercial but well worth visiting when you're in the area. Suggest that you approach from the north since the southern approaches are quite smoggy much of the year.

No. on figure	Name or location	Temperature of water (°F)	Flow (gallons per minute)	Associated rocks	References on chemical quality	Remarks and additional references
	Nevada					
1	T. 46 N., R. 27 E., 12 miles west of Pine Forest Range.	108	Small	Lava (Tertiary)		Ref. 441.
2	Bog Ranch Hot Springs, on north side of Thousand Creek Valley 6 miles southwest of Denio, Oregon.	130; 190	20	Intrusive granite (Jurassic)		2 springs. Refs. 144, 403, 441.
3	T. 47 N., R. 31 E., south of Steens Mountain.	178		do		2 springs. Refs. 144, 441.
4	T. 45 N., R. 32 E., 12 miles north of Mason's Crossing of Quinn River.	118	Small	do		
5	T. 45 N., R. 32 E., 11 miles north of Quinn River (town).	130	150	do		Deposit of siliceous sinter. Ref. 440, also field notes by G. A. Waring.
6	T. 45 N., R. 33 E., on west side of King River valley.	76; 80		Lava (upper Tertiary)		2 springs. Water used locally. Refs. 144, 441.
6A	Cordero Mine	118; 138		do		2 pumped wells, 550 and 580 ft deep. Water used at mine. Ref. 451.
7	T. 45 N., R. 41 E., at head of North Fork of Little Humboldt River.	Hot		Lava (Tertiary)		Ref. 144.
8	T. 40 N., R. 25 E., at Soldier Meadows, 15 miles south of old Camp McGarry.	Hot		do		Several springs. Ref. 144.
9	T. 40 N., R. 28 E., west of sink of Quinn River, at west edge of Black Rock Desert.	60		Alluvium near lava		2 springs. Water supply for prospectors. Refs. 144, 418.
10	T. 43 N., R. 31 E., 7 miles west of Mason's Crossing of Quinn River.	155		Lava (upper Tertiary)		Several springs. Ref. 144; also field notes by G. A. Waring.
10A	Near south bank of Quinn River	Warm	Small	Alluvium		Data from field notes by G. A. Waring.
11	T. 41 N., R. 41 E., on bank of Little Humboldt River, 12 miles southeast of Paradise Valley post office.	130		do		
11A	Near North and South Forks of Little Humboldt River, 25 miles east of Paradise Valley.	Hot	Small	do		
12	Double Hot Springs, in T. 37 N., R. 24 E., on west flank of Black Rock Range.	165–191	5	Faulted(?) lava (Tertiary) overlying granite.		Several springs. Refs. 144, 418, 451.

No. on figure	Name or location	Temperature of water (°F)	Flow (gallons per minute)	Associated rocks	References on chemical quality	Remarks and additional references
				Nevada—Continued		
12A	Near base of west flank of Black Rock Range.	130–150	3	Faulted (?) lava (Tertiary) overlying granite.		3 springs, 1-2 miles apart. Ref. 451.
13	T. 37 N., R. 25 E., on southeast side of Black Rock Range.	Hot		____do____		Several springs. Ref. 441.
14	T. 37 N., R. 26 E., in arm of Black Rock Desert.	Hot		Alluvium near lava____		Ref. 441.
15	Van Riper, in T. 36 N., R. 24 E., on southwest side of Black Rock Range.	145	50	Lava (Tertiary) overlying granite.		3 springs. Ref. 144.
16	T. 36 N., R. 25 E., at south end of Black Rock Range, 10 miles southeast of Division Peak.	Hot		Lava (Tertiary)____		Several springs. Ref. 144.
17	Secs. 16, 21, 24, 34, T. 36 N., R. 26 E., on west border of Black Rock Desert.	Hot		Alluvium (Quaternary) near lava (Tertiary).		Several springs. Refs. 144, 438.
18	2 miles north of Winnemucca____	Hot	Small	Mesozoic strata____		Water used locally. Ref. 386.
19	Golconda Hot Springs, in T. 36 N., R. 40 E.	120–150	250	Alluvium____		About 12 springs. Resort. Refs. 109, 144, 422, 437.
19A	Blossom Hot Spring, in sec. 10, T. 35 N., R. 43 E., 8 miles north of Valmy.	107	70	____do____		Rises in broad deep pool. Water supply for cattle.
19B 19C 19D 19E 19F 19G	Humboldt River Valley____	Warm	Small	____do____		Data from field notes by G. A. Waring.
20	T. 39 N., R. 40 E., at head of South Fork of Little Humboldt River.	Hot	Small	Lava (Tertiary)____		Ref. 144.
21	Sec. 30, T. 45 N., R. 54 E., 5 miles southeast of Mountain City.	104–106	20	Limestone (Paleozoic)____		4 springs. Water used for bathing.
22	Sec. 23, T. 46 N., R 56 E., 15 miles east of Mountain City.	104	55	Limestone (Paleozoic)____		Several springs. Water used locally.
22A	1.5 miles north of Contact____	133	5	Lava (Tertiary)____		Several springs and shallow wells. Water used for bathing.
22B	Mineral (San Jacinto) Spring____	78–126	1,200	Lake beds (Tertiary) overlying Paleozoic strata.		Water used locally.
23	Sec. 22, T. 47 N., R. 68 E., on west side of Goose Creek.	57	850	Cherty limestone (Paleozoic).		Forms boggy area at edge of Goose Creek Meadow.
24	Nile Spring, in sec. 30, T. 47 N., R. 70 E., on east side of Goose Creek.	106	6	Alluvium____		Do.
25	Gamble's Hole, in sec. 10, T. 46 N., R. 69 E., on east side of Goose Creek.	103	8	____do____		Several springs in 1-acre area.
26	Sec. 26, T. 46 N., R. 69 E., at head of main fork of Spring Creek.	62	200	Rhyolite (Tertiary)____		Ref. 144.
27	T. 41 N., R. 69 E., at south end of Thousand Springs Valley.	Boiling		Carboniferous strata____		4 springs. Water used for sheep dipping. Large mound of tufa. Refs. 138, 430; also field notes by G. A. Waring.
28	Hot Creek mining district in T. 39 N., R. 60 E., on Marys River 15 miles north of Deeth.	110–122	30	____do____		Data from field notes by G. A. Waring.
29	Cress Ranch, in sec. 14, T. 38 N., R. 59 E., 8 miles north of Deeth.	Hot	Small	Near lava (Tertiary)____		Water contains much H₂S. Used for bathing. Ref. 144, also field notes by G. A. Waring.
30	Sec. 21, T. 38 N., R. 62 E., in Emigrant Canyon, 4.2 miles north of Wells.	98	50	Faulted quartzite (Carboniferous).		3 main springs. Large deposit of tufa. Water supply for cattle. Data from field notes by G. A. Waring.
30A	5.5 miles north of Wells____	113–122	10	Carboniferous strata____		Several springs in canyon. Water used for irrigation. Data from field notes by G. A. Waring.
30B	Metropolis____	102	800	Limestone (Carboniferous)____		Water used for domestic supply and for irrigation. Ref. 451.
30C	Johnson Ranch____	73	30	Lava (Tertiary)____		Many springs. Deposit of tufa. Ref. 451.
30D	H. D. Ranch____	142–154	600	____do____		3 springs. Water used for bathing. Refs. 138, 144; also field notes by G. A. Waring.
31	Hot Springs, in T. 33 N., R. 53 E., 9 miles northwest of Carlin.	98	15	Quartzite (Carboniferous)____		Several springs. Water used for bathing. Ref. 138.
32	Elko Hot Springs, in T. 34 N., R. 55 E., 1 mile west of Elko.	192		Carboniferous strata____	137	Several springs. Water used locally. Ref. 144.
33	T. 33 N., R. 58 E., 8 miles southwest of Fort Halleck.	Warm		Alluvium near lava____		Water used locally. Refs. 138, 421.
34	T. 34 N., R. 62 E., near Warm Creek in Independence Valley.	Warm	250	Alluvium (Quaternary) near Carboniferous strata.		Several springs. Refs. 415, 418, 424.
34A	Near east side of Ruby Lake____	Hot	Small	Alluvium____		Several springs. Refs. 144, 418.
35	Miller's Hot Springs, in T. 30 N., R. 59 E., at northeast end of Franklin Lake.	170		Alluvium (Quaternary) near lava.		Water irrigates meadow.
35A	Hill's Warm Spring, in sec. 18, T. 44 N., R. 20 E., 10 miles north of Vya.	83	10	Alluvium____		Do.
35B	Hill's Spring, in sec. 11, T. 43 N., R. 19 E., 5 miles north of Vya.	66	8	____do____		Water used for irrigation.
35C	Twin Springs, in sec. 4, T. 42 N., R. 19 E., at Vya.	70	200	Lake beds (Pliocene?)____		Ref. 441.
36	T. 38 N., R. 18 E., at south end of Surprise Valley.	Hot		Lava (Tertiary)____		Many springs in 75-acre area. Largest hot springs in northwestern part of Nevada. Water used for irrigation. Sandy mounds and deposits of tufa. Refs. 144, 409, 418.
37	Wards' (Fly Ranch) Hot Springs, in T. 34 N., R. 23 E., at northwest end of Alkali Flat and 5 miles northeast of Granite Peak.	60 to boiling		Alluvium near granite____	128	Many springs. Water used for bathing. Ref. 436.
38	Gerlach Hot Springs, 1 mile northwest of Gerlach.	188–194		____do____	144, 409	Several springs. Ref. 441.
39	Mud Springs, 2 miles west of Gerlach____	Hot		____do____		Also several flowing wells. Water used for irrigation. Ref. 441.
40	Deep Hole Spring, in sec. 25, T. 33 N., R. 22 E., at north end of Smoke Creek Desert.	62	30	Lake beds (Quaternary)____		Do.
41	Wall Spring, in sec. 3, T. 32 N., R. 21 E., on northwest side of Smoke Creek Desert.	Warm		____do____		Ref. 441.
42	Buffalo Spring, in T. 31 N., R. 20 E., on west side of Smoke Creek Desert.	Warm		____do____		

No. on figure	Name or location	Temperature of water (°F)	Flow (gallons per minute)	Associated rocks	References on chemical quality	Remarks and additional references

Nevada—Continued

No. on figure	Name or location	Temperature of water (°F)	Flow (gallons per minute)	Associated rocks	References on chemical quality	Remarks and additional references
43	Buckbrush Spring, in T. 29 N., R. 19 E., on west side of Smoke Creek Desert.	Warm	----------	Lake beds (Quaternary)	----------	Ref. 441.
44	Rotten Egg Spring, in T. 29 N., R. 19 E., on southwest side of Smoke Creek Desert.	92	10	----do	----------	Water smells strongly of H_2S. Ref. 441.
45	Round Hole Spring, in sec. 31, T. 29 N., R. 19 E., on southwest side of Smoke Creek Desert.	Warm	----------	----do	----------	Also several flowing wells. Ref. 441.
46	Ross Spring, in T. 28 N., R. 20 E., at south end of Smoke Creek Desert.	Hot	----------	Lava (Tertiary)	----------	Refs. 144, 441.
47	T. 28 N., R. 21 E., near north end of Pyramid Lake.	Hot	----------	----do	----------	Several springs. Refs. 144, 441.
48	Fish Spring, in T. 26 N., R. 19 E., 10 miles northwest of Pyramid railroad station.	Warm	----------	----do	----------	Ref. 441.
49	T. 26 N., R. 20 E., on northwest side of Pyramid Lake.	206–208	----------	Faulted lava (Tertiary)	----------	Several springs. Refs. 144, 441.
50	T. 27 N., R. 23 E., on northwest shore of Winnemucca Lake.	Warm	----------	Lava (Tertiary)	----------	Several springs. Ref. 441.
51	T. 26 N., R. 23 E., on west shore of Winnemucca Lake.	Warm	----------	----do	----------	Do.
52	T. 24 N., R. 22 E., on Anaho Island in Pyramid Lake.	120	----------	----do	----------	Several springs.
53	Cottonwood Spring, in sec. 26, T. 23 N., R. 21 E., in Warm Spring Valley 3 miles south of Dewey.	Warm	----------	Lava (Tertiary) overlying granite.	----------	Water used locally.
54	T. 21 N., R. 24 E., in Dead Ox Canyon 12 miles south of Dixon.	Warm	----------	Lava (Tertiary)	----------	
55	Lawton Hot Springs, 6 miles west of Reno.	120	250	Faulted granite	137	2 main springs. Water used for bathing. Resort.
55A	Moana Springs, 2 miles south of Reno.	100–200	----------	Metamorphic rocks	----------	Wells. Water used for bathing. Ref. 451.
55B	Huffaker Springs, 5 miles southeast of Moana bathing resort.	79–81	10	Alluvium	----------	Several springs on bank of creek. Ref. 451.
55C	Zoleggi Springs, 3 miles southwest of Huffaker Springs (no. 55B).	103	125	----do	----------	Several springs. Ref. 451.
55D	Da Monte Springs, 1.5 miles east of Zoleggi Springs.	130	40	----do	----------	On bank of creek. Ref. 451.
55E	Mount Rose, 10 miles south of Reno.	Hot	----------	Metamorphic rocks	----------	Erupting wells. Resort. Ref. 451.
55F	Reno Hot Springs, 10.5 miles south of Reno.	Hot	----------	----do	----------	Drilled wells. Resort. Ref. 451.
56	Steamboat Springs, in sec. 33, T. 18 N., R. 20 E., 11 miles south of Reno.	167–203	300	Granite	20, 128, 137, 427, 452, 562.	Many springs, including 3 small geysers. Resort and sanitarium. Refs. 400, 401, 404–406, 413, 417, 418, 420, 424, 426, 436, 448–450, 453–456.
57	Bowers Mansion (Franktown Hot) Spring; 10 miles north of Carson City.	115–118	75	Faulted Granite	137	Resort. Ref. 144.
58	T. 19 N., R. 23 E., 10 miles southwest of Wadsworth.	73	----------	Lava (Tertiary)	----------	Water used locally Refs. 144, 418.
59	Carson (Swift's, Shaw's) Hot Springs, 2 miles north of Carson City.	120	75	Metamorphic rocks	137	Water used for bathing. Resort. Ref. 144.
59A	Nevada State Prison	Warm	----------	Lake beds (Pleistocene)	----------	Water used locally.
60	Walley's (Genoa) Hot Springs, 6 miles northwest of Minden.	136–160	Large	Faulted granite	133, 137	Many springs. Resort. Refs. 125, 144, 428.
61	Hind's Hot Springs, in sec. 16, T. 12 N., R. 23 E., near Simpson.	60–143	550	Alluvium overlying granite	----------	Several springs. Water used for irrigation. Resort. Refs. 144, 429.
62	Wabuska Springs, in T. 15 N., R. 25 E., 1 mile north of Wabuska.	138–162	----------	Lava (Tertiary) overlying granite(?).	----------	Several springs. Water used locally. Ref. 144.
63	Butte Spring, in T. 33 N., R. 26 E., at north end of Hot Springs Butte, 25 miles southwest of Sulphur.	182	20	Granite	----------	Refs. 144, 441.
63A	Near Humboldt River, 2 miles north of Mill City.	Warm	Small	Alluvium	----------	Several springs.
64	Leach's (Pleasant Valley) Hot Springs in sec. 35, T. 32 N., R. 38 E., in Grass Valley 25 miles south of Winnemucca.	158–202	200	Alluvium overlying Mesozoic strata.	----------	Several springs. Water used locally. Deposit of siliceous sinter. Ref. 424; also field notes by G. A. Waring.
65	Guthrie (Nelson) Springs, in sec. 36, T. 32 N., R. 38 E., 25 miles south of Winnemucca.	139–204	250	Alluvium near basalt (Quaternary).	412	8 pools in 1-acre area; also several other springs. Water is sulfurous. Used for irrigation. Deposits of tufa and siliceous sinter. Ref. 144 and field notes by G. A. Waring.
66	Kyle's Hot Springs, in sec. 2, T. 39 N., R. 36 E., 25 miles southeast of Humboldt.	100–160	Small	Alluvium	----------	Several springs. Deposit of sinter. Former resort. Ref. 144.
66A	Miller Ranch	58–61	900	----do	----------	Several springs. Water used for irrigation. Data from field notes by G. A. Waring.
67	Sec. 1, T. 25 N., R. 36 E., near north end of Salt Marsh (Osobb) Valley.	Hot	----------	Contact of Mesozoic strata with underlying granite.	----------	Ref. 438.
68	Sou (Gilbert's) Hot Springs, in sec. 29, T. 26 N., R. 38 E., near north end of Salt Marsh (Osobb) Valley.	160–185	----------	Faulted(?) lava (Tertiary)	----------	Several springs issuing from tufa mounds in 12-acre area. Refs. 144, 418, 438, 442.
69	Cone Spring, in sec. 26, T. 25 N., R. 38 E., in Salt Marsh (Osobb) Valley.	125	Small	Lava (Tertiary)	----------	
	Sec. 35, T. 25 N., R. 38 E., 0.25 mile from Cone Spring, in Salt Marsh (Osobb) Valley.	----------	----------	----------	----------	
70	T. 24 N., R. 36 E., on northwest side of Salt Marsh (Osobb) Valley.	Warm	Small	Lava (Tertiary) overlying granite.	----------	Ref. 441.
71	T. 23 N., R. 35 E., on northeast side of Pah Ute Mountains.	Hot	Small	Alluvium near granite	----------	Several springs.
71A	5 miles south-southwest of spring No. 71.	Warm	Small	Granite	----------	
72	Springer's (Brady's, Fernley) Hot Springs, in sec. 12, T. 22 N., R. 26 E., on U.S. Highway 40.	158–209	50	Lake beds (Quaternary) near lava (Tertiary).	409	Several springs. Deposit of siliceous sinter. Water used for bathing. Also as water supply for auto station.
73	Eagle Salt Works Springs, in T. 20 N., R. 27 E., 15 miles northwest of Fallon.	----------	----------	Alluvium	----------	Several springs. Water used locally.
74	Borax Spring, in T. 17 N., R. 30 E., 3 miles east of South Carson Lake.	178	----------	Alluvium near lava (late Tertiary).	----------	Ref. 144.
74A	Lee Springs, 18 miles south of Fallon	172	25	----do	----------	Deposit of siliceous sinter. Also a well. Ref. 451.

No. on figure	Name or location	Temperature of water (°F)	Flow (gallons per minute)	Associated rocks	References on chemical quality	Remarks and additional references
				Nevada—Continued		
75	Sec. 6, T. 16 N., R. 32 E., 20 miles southeast of Fallon.	Hot		Lava (Tertiary)		Several springs. Water smells of H₂S. Ref. 144.
76	Izzenhood Ranch Springs, in T. 36 N., R. 45 E., 25 miles north of Battle Mountain.	83	1,000	___do___		Water level lowered 4 ft by trenching, thus doubling original discharge. Water used for irrigation. Ref. 425.
77	White Rock Spring, in sec. 8, T. 33 N., R. 47 E., 2 miles west of Rock Creek.	Warm		___do___		Water used locally. Refs. 144, 434.
77A	Beowawe Geysers, in sec. 5, T. 31 N., R. 48 E., in Whirlwind Valley 8 miles west of Beowawe.	120 to boiling	100	Faulted basalt (Tertiary)	435, 562	About 50 springs and mud pools on hillside tufa terrace 0.75 mile long, also 3 springs in nearby lowland. 2 or 3 springs show true geyser action, 1 spouting to height of 30 ft. Refs. 410, 414, 434, 435.
78	Sec. 24, T. 29 N., R. 41 E., in Buffalo Valley 25 miles southwest of Battle Mountain (town).	130	5	Lava (Tertiary)	446	Several springs. Ref. 438.
79	Mound Spring, in sec. 7, T. 28 N., R. 44 E., in Reese River valley 25 miles south of Battle Mountain (town).	110	3	___do___		Water used for roadside watering.
80	Sec. 23, T. 27 N., R. 43 E., 1 mile north of Hot Spring Ranch in Reese River valley.	124	450	___do___	446	Several springs. Water used for irrigation. Ref. 418.
81	Sec. 26, T. 27 N., R. 43 E., at Hot Spring Ranch.	122	50	___do___	446	Several springs. Water used for domestic purposes and irrigation. Ref. 418.
82	T. 27 N., R. 47 E., 10 miles south of Lander.	Hot		Lava intrusive (Tertiary) in Carboniferous strata.		Water used locally. Refs. 138, 435.
83	T. 22 N., R. 47 E., near north end of Grass Valley.	181		Devonian strata.		Water used locally. Refs. 144, 424.
84	T. 18 N., R. 39 E., in Smith Creek valley 6 miles north of Hot Springs.	Warm	Small	Lava (Tertiary)		Water used locally. Refs. 128, 144, 409, 441.
85	Sec. 25, T. 17 N., R. 40 E., on west side of Smith Creek valley.	Hot		___do___		Several springs. Ref. 144.
86	Spencer Hot Springs, in T. 17 N., R. 46 E., 18 miles southeast of Austin.	117–144	6	___do___	432	Several springs. Water used locally. Refs. 433, 447.
87	Sec. 14, T. 16 N., R. 45 E., 20 miles southeast of Austin.	Hot	5	___do___		7 springs. Water used for bathing.
88	Horseshoe Ranch Springs, 1 mile northeast of Beowawe.	125–132	30	Faulted lava (Tertiary)		2 springs. Water used for bathing and irrigation.
88A	Sec. 2, T. 29 N., R. 48 E., in Crescent Valley 12 miles south of Beowawe.	122	40	Lava (Tertiary) overlying Paleozoic strata.		2 springs. Water supply for cattle.
89	Sec. 12, T. 28 N., R. 52 E., at head of Hot Creek, 14 miles north of Mineral.	84	5,900	Lake beds (Pliocene) overlying Paleozoic strata.		6 springs. Water used for irrigation.
90	Carlotti Ranch Springs, in sec. 24, T. 28 N., R. 52 E., 10 miles north of Mineral.	95; 102	100	___do___		2 springs, 0.25 mile apart. Water used for irrigation.
99A	Bruffey's (Mineral Hill) Hot Springs, in sec. 14, T. 27 N., R. 52 E., 7 miles northeast of Mineral.	108–152	50	___do___		6 springs. Water used for domestic purposes and irrigation. Ref. 144.
91	Flynn Ranch Springs, in sec. 5, T. 25 N., R. 53 E., in Diamond Valley.	69–78	10	Alluvium		Deep pool and minor springs. Water used for irrigation.
91A	Siri Ranch Spring, in sec. 6, T. 24 N., R. 53 E., in Diamond Valley.	87	300	___do___		Water used for irrigation.
91B	Sadler (Big Shipley) Springs, in sec. 23, T. 24 N., 52 E., in Diamond Valley.	103–106	5,000	Alluvium near faulted Paleozoic strata.		Several springs. Water used for irrigation. Refs. 138, 144.
91C	Sulphur Springs, in sec. 36, T. 23 N., R. 52 E., on Sulphur Springs Ranch in Diamond Valley.	74	20	___do___		2 main springs. Water used for irrigation.
91D	Jacobson Ranch Springs, on east side of Diamond Valley.	71–75	900	___do___		Several springs. Water used for irrigation.
92	Sec. 15, T. 24 N., R. 47 E., on west side of Grass Valley.	Hot	Small	___do___		Several springs. Water supply for cattle.
93	Sec. 33, T. 24 N., R. 48 E., on east side of Grass Valley.	Hot	Small	___do___		Several springs.
93A	Bartine Hot Springs, in sec. 5, T. 19 N., R. 50 E., in Antelope Valley 35 miles west of Eureka.	105; 108	10	Lake beds (Tertiary) near faulted Tertiary strata.		2 springs issuing from large mound of tufa. Also a flowing well. Water used locally.
93B	Clobe Hot Spring, in sec. 28, T. 18 N., R. 50 E., in Antelope Valley, 45 miles southwest of Eureka.	142	100	Alluvium near hills of faulted lava.		Water supply for cattle.
93C	Sara Ranch Springs, in sec. 7, T. 16 N., R. 53 E., at head of Fish Creek.	66	4,000	Alluvium		About 20 deep pools in area 0.5 mile in diameter. Water used for irrigation.
94	Collar and Elbow Spring, in sec. 27, T. 26 N., R. 65 E., near north end of Steptoe Valley.	92	20	___do___	406, 408	Deposit of tufa.
95	Cherry Creek (Young's) Hot Springs, in T. 23 N., R. 63 E., 1.2 miles southwest of Cherry Creek (town) in Steptoe Valley.	118–135	40	Alluvium near Paleozoic strata.	406, 408	3 springs. Water used for bathing.
96	Shellbourne Hot Springs, in T. 23 N., R. 63 E., about 100 ft from Cherry Creek (Young's) Hot Springs (No. 95).	124; 135		___do___	408	2 springs. Water used for bathing and irrigation.
97	Borchert John Spring, in sec. 16, T. 22 N., R. 63 E., in Steptoe Valley.	66	800	Talus deposit	408	Water used for irrigation.
98	Monte Neva (Goodrich, Melvin) Hot Springs, in sec. 24, T. 31 N., R. 63 E., 1 mile northwest of Warm Springs railroad station in Steptoe Valley.	173–193	625	Alluvium near Paleozoic strata.	406, 408	6 springs issuing from mound of siliceous sinter.
99	T. 21 N., R. 70 E., at east base of Kern Mountains.	Warm		Faulted Paleozoic strata		Ref. 138.
100	Sec. 5, T. 19 N., R. 63 E., 10 miles northwest of McGill.	58–76	200	Carboniferous strata	408	Several springs. Water used for irrigation.
101	McGill Warm Springs, in sec. 21, T. 18 N., R. 64 E., 0.75 mile west of McGill.	76–84	450	Alluvium near Paleozoic strata.	406, 408	3 main springs. Water used for irrigation.
102	Ely Warm Spring, in sec. 10, T. 16 N., R. 63 E., 1.5 miles northeast of Ely.	85	23	___do___	406	Water used for bathing. Ref. 408.
102A	Moore's Ranch Springs, in T. 23 N., R. 56 E., in Newark Valley.	65–70	200	Alluvium		Several springs. Water used for irrigation.
103	Big Blue Spring, in sec. 23, T. 14 N., R. 56 E., near the north end of White Pine Valley.	Warm		Paleozoic strata	144	Water used for bathing.

No. on figure	Name or location	Temperature of water (°F)	Flow (gallons per minute)	Associated rocks	References on chemical quality	Remarks and additional references
				Nevada—Continued		
103A	Williams Hot Springs, in sec. 33, T. 13 N., R. 60 E., 12 miles northwest of Preston.	124; 128	185	Alluvium		2 springs. Water used for irrigation. Ref. 431.
104	Preston Springs, in sec. 1, T., 12 N., R. 61 E.	72	5,700	Alluvium near Paleozoic strata.		Several springs. Water used for domestic purposes and irrigation. Refs. 407, 421, 431.
105	Lund Spring, in sec. 33, T. 12 N., R. 62 E.	66	2,400	____do		Water supply for town. Also used for irrigation. Refs. 407, 421, 431.
106	Warm Sulphur Springs, in T. 11 N., R. 65 E., at head of Warm Creek.	Warm	972	Paleozoic strata		Several springs. Water used for irrigation Refs. 138, 144, 421.
107	Big Spring, in T. 11 N., R. 69 E., in Snake Valley, 15 miles south of Baker.	64	8,000, 12,000	Limestone (Cambrian)		Water used for irrigation. Ref. 141.
107A	Sec. 30, T. 10 N., R. 70 E., at head of Big Springs Creek.	Warm	2,000	Alluvium		Water used for irrigation.
108	Double Spring, in T. 13 N., R. 29 E., 3 miles north of Walker Lake.	Warm		Lava (Tertiary)		Refs. 144, 441.
109	Sec. 4, T. 7 N., R. 27 E., on East Walker River, 20 miles west of Hawthorne.	Hot		Granite near lava		Several springs. Water used for bathing. State reserve.
110	T. 6 N., R. 35 E., at Sodaville	80–101	100	Alluvium		Several springs. Water used locally. Refs. 419, 423.
111	Waterworks Springs, in sec. 22, T. 2 S., R. 39 E., at Silver Peak.	69–118	500	Lava (Tertiary)	432	11 Springs. Water supply for town. Refs. 411, 444, 445.
112	Alkali Spring, in sec. 26, T. 1 S., R. 41 E., 11 miles northwest of Goldfield.	120–140	50	Alluvium near Paleozoic strata.	399, 432, 439	Deposit of tufa.
113	Wedell Springs, in sec. 7, T. 12 N., R. 34 E., 12 miles southeast of Rawhide.	129; 144	60	Alluvium overlying lava (Tertiary).		2 main springs. Water used locally. Refs. 138, 144.
114	T. 14 N., R. 43 E., 1 mile east of McLeod's Ranch in Big Smoky Valley.	Hot		Alluvium near Paleozoic strata.		Issues from large mound. Ref. 432.
115	Gendron Spring, in T. 14 N., R. 43 E., near Millett in Big Smoky Valley.	61	10	____do	432	Water used locally.
116	Charnock (Big Blue) Springs, in T. 13 N., R. 44 E., near Charnock Ranch.	80	450	Alluvium overlying lava (Tertiary).		Several springs issuing from large mound. Water used for irrigation. Ref. 432.
117	Sec. 14, T. 11 N., R. 42 E., in Big Smoky Valley, 14 miles south of Millett.	Boiling	600	Faulted lava (Tertiary)		Water used locally. Refs. 144, 432.
118	Darrough Hot Springs, in sec. 17, T. 11 N., R. 43 E., on Darrough Ranch in Big Smoky Valley.	160–207	200	Alluvium near Paleozoic strata.	432	Several springs. Resort. Ref. 433.
119	Sec. 1, T. 14 N., R. 47 E., 2 miles southeast of Potts.	Warm		Lava (Tertiary)		Several springs. Water used locally.
120	Diana's Punch Bowl, in sec. 22, T. 14 N., R. 47 E., 5 miles south of Potts.	Hot	Small	Alluvium (Quaternary) near lava (Tertiary).		
121	Fish Springs, in secs. 26 and 35, T. 11 N., R. 49 E., in Fish Creek valley.	Warm		Lava (Tertiary)		Several springs. Water used locally. Ref. 144.
122	Sec. 32, T. 13 N., R. 56 E., 5 miles north of Duckwater.	Warm	Large	Alluvium		Several springs. Water used for irrigation.
123	Indian Springs, in T. 7 N., R. 42 E., near San Antonio.	Warm		Lava (Tertiary) overlying Paleozoic strata.		3 springs. Water used locally. Ref. 138.
124	T. 7 N., R. 51 E., on Hot Creek 8 miles northeast of Tybo.	Warm		____do		Several springs issuing from terrace of tufa.
125	T. 4 N., R. 50 E., near south end of Hot Creek valley.	Boiling		Lava (Tertiary) overlying Silurian and Devonian strata.		2 springs. Ref. 144.
126	Lock's Springs, in sec. 15, T. 8 N., R. 55 E., on west side of Railroad Valley 20 miles southwest of Currant.	93–99	2,000	Alluvium near faulted(?) lava (Tertiary).		2 springs issuing in pools on terrace of tufa and 2 springs in meadow at base of terrace. Water used for irrigation.
127	Chimney Springs, in sec. 16, T. 7 N., R. 55 E., in Railroad Valley 6 miles south of Lock's Springs (No. 126).	130–160	100	Alluvium near faulted(?) lava (Tertiary).		3 springs issuing from mounds of tufa. Water supply for cattle.
128	Blue Eagle Springs, in sec. 11, T. 8 N., R. 57 E., on east side of Railroad Valley 18 miles south of Currant.	82	1,385	Alluvium		2 main springs. Water used for irrigation. Ref. 407.
129	Kate Spring, in sec. 14, T. 8 N., R. 57 E., 0.75 mile south of Blue Eagle Springs (No. 128).	73	14	____do		Water used for domestic purposes and irrigation.
130	Butterfield Springs, in sec. 27, T. 8 N., R. 57 E., on east side of Railroad Valley.	64	227	____do		2 springs. Water used for irrigation.
131	Bacon Springs, in sec. 34, T. 8 N., R. 57 E., on east side of Railroad Valley.	57	2	____do		2 springs. Water supply for cattle.
132	Bullwhacker Spring, in sec. 28, T. 7 N., R. 57 E., on east side of Railroad Valley.	59	10	____do		Water supply for cattle.
133	Willow Springs, in sec. 5, T. 6 N., R. 57 E., on east side of Railroad Valley.	60	30	____do		2 springs. Water supply for cattle.
134	Mormon Springs, in sec. 33, T. 9 N., R. 61 E., 5 miles west of White River.	100	100	____do		Several springs. Water used for irrigation. Ref. 431.
134A	Moon River Springs	92	900	____do		Water used for irrigation. Ref. 431.
135	Riordan Ranch (Emigrant) Springs, in T. 9 N., R. 62 E., near White River.	70	200	____do		Several springs. Water used for irrigation.
136	White River Valley (Flag, Sunnyside) Springs, in secs. 28, 31, and 32, T. 7 N., R. 62 E., on Whipple and Hendricks Ranches.	65–75	2,000	____do		6 springs. Water used for irrigation. Refs. 144, 407.
137	Hot Creek Ranch Springs, in sec. 18, T. 6 N., R. 61 E., in White River valley 8 miles southwest of Sunnyside.	85–90	5,000	____do		Several springs. Water used for irrigation. Refs. 144, 407, 431, 443.
138	Hicks Hot Springs, in T. 11 S., R. 47 E., 5 miles north of Beatty.	110	40	Lava (Tertiary) overlying Paleozoic strata.		5 springs. Water used for bathing. Ref. 399.
139	Ash Meadow Springs, in sec. 22, T. 17 S., R. 50 E.	76–94	450	Alluvium near Cambrian strata.		4 springs. Refs. 144, 399.
140	Pahrump Springs, in sec. 14, T. 20 S., R. 53 E., on Pahrump Ranch.	77	2,200	Alluvium near faulted Paleozoic strata.	447	2 springs. Water used for irrigation. Refs. 398, 443.
141	Manse Springs, in sec. 3, T. 21 S., R. 54 E., on Manse Ranch.	75	1,500	____do	447	2 springs. Water used for irrigation. Ref. 269.
142	Geyser Ranch Springs, in T. 8 N., R. 65 E., 5 miles east of Patterson.	65–70	50	Alluvium near lava (Tertiary).	407	Several springs. Water used for irrigation. Refs. 138, 144.
143	T. 5 N., R. 70 E., on Hammond Ranch	84		Limestone (Paleozoic)		Several springs. Water used for irrigation. Ref. 407.

No. on figure	Name or location	Temperature of water (°F)	Flow (gallons per minute)	Associated rocks	References on chemical quality	Remarks and additional references
				Nevada—Continued		
144	Bennetts Springs, in T. 2 S., R. 66 E., 9 miles west of Panaca.	70	Small	Alluvium near limestone (Paleozoic).		2 springs. Water supply for cattle. Ref. 407.
144A	Delmue's Springs, 10 miles north of Panaca	70	200	Lava (Tertiary)		2 springs. Water used for irrigation.
144B	Flatnose Ranch	70	100	...do		Water used for irrigation.
145	Panaca Spring, in sec. 4, T. 2 S., R. 68 E.	85–88	2,500	Faulted Paleozoic strata	407	Several springs. Water supply for town.
146	Caliente Hot Spring, in T. 4 S., R. 67 E., 0.25 mile north of Caliente.	110		...do		Formerly flowed, now pumped. Water used for bathing.
147	Hiko Spring, in sec. 22, T. 4 S., R. 60 E.	90	4,000	...do	407, 441	Water used for domestic purposes and irrigation. Refs. 141, 144.
148	Crystal Spring, 1 mile northwest of Hiko	90	9,000	...do		Water used for domestic purposes and irrigation. Ref. 141.
149	Ash (Alamo) Spring, 4 miles south of Hiko.	90–97	9,000	...do		6 main springs. Water used for domestic purposes and irrigation. Ref. 141.
150	T. 14 S., R. 65 E., 3 miles west of Moapa	90		Limestone (Paleozoic)		Several springs. Water used for bathing and irrigation. Ref. 407.
151	Indian Spring, in sec. 16, T. 16 S., R. 56 E., 1 mile south of Indian Spring railroad station.	78	410	...do	407, 443	Water supply for railroad; also used for irrigation. Ref. 398.
152	Las Vegas Springs, in T. 20 S., R. 61 E., 2 miles west of Las Vegas.	73	2,600	Pleistocene strata	407, 421	2 springs. Water used for domestic and industrial purposes, also for irrigation. Refs. 144, 269.

Washington palms grace the tranquil waterways that emanate from Warner Hot Springs.

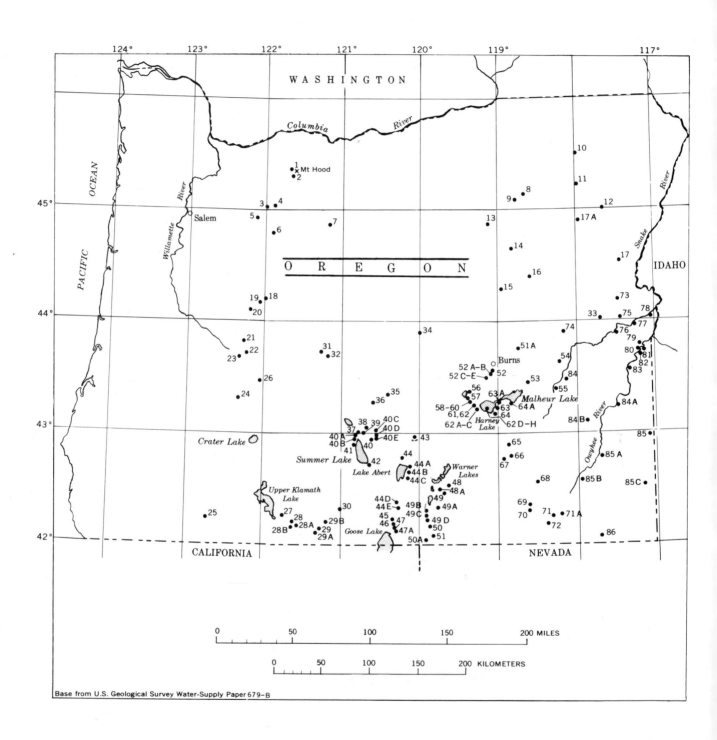

WASHINGTON

Columbia River

OCEAN

PACIFIC

124° 123° 122° 121° 120° 119° 117°

1
× Mt Hood
2

10

11

9 • 8

12

17A

17

Snake River

IDAHO

45°

3 • 4

5

6

7

13

14

16

15

Salem

Willamette River

O R E G O N

19 • 18
20

44°

21
22
23

31
32

34

51A

73

33 75 78

74 76 79

54 84 80 81
82
83

Burns

52 A–B
52 C–E 52

53

55

26

24

Crater Lake

35
36

56
57

63A

84

58–60
61,62
62 A–C

63
64 64A

Malheur Lake

Harney
Lake 62 D–H

84A

84B Owyhee River

43°

38 39 40C
37 40D
40 A 40E
40 B 43
40 41

Summer Lake

44

42

Lake Abert

44 A
44 B
44 C

Warner
Lakes

48
48 A

65

66 67

85

85 A

68 85 B 85C

Upper Klamath
Lake

30

44D
44 E

49

85

25

27
28
28B 28A

29B
29

Goose Lake

45 47
46 47A

50A

49B
49C

49 A

49 D
50
51

69
70 71 71A

72

86

42°

29A

CALIFORNIA

NEVADA

0 50 100 150 200 MILES

0 50 100 150 200 KILOMETERS

Base from U.S. Geological Survey Water-Supply Paper 679–B

66

Oregon

No.	Location	Temp.	Flow	Geology	Ref.	Remarks
1	Sec. 29, T. 2 S., R. 9 E., in crater of Mount Hood.	120–194		Lava (Quaternary)		Many fumaroles emitting steam and gases, including H₂S. Refs. 479, 484, 485.
2	Mount Hood Warm Springs, in sec. 24, T. 3 S., R. 8½ E., on south side of Mount Hood.	60–80	25	..do..		Several small springs in 3-acre area. Resort.
3	Sec. 25, T. 6 S., R. 6 E., on the Clackamas River.	188 (max)		Columbia River Basalt (Tertiary).		Several springs. Water used locally. Ref. 481.
4	Carey (Austin) Hot Springs, in sec. 30, T. 6 S., R. 7 E., on the Clackamas River.	176–196		..do..		Several springs. Water smells of H₂S. Used for bathing. Ref. 481.
5	Bagsby Hot Springs, in sec. 26, T. 7 S., R. 5 E., on Hot Springs Creek 4 miles south of Thunder Mountain.	Hot	50	..do..		8 springs in 5-acre area. Campground. Ref. 481.
6	Breitenbush Hot Springs, in sec. 20, T. 9 S., R. 7 E., on the Breitenbush River.	140–198	900	..do..		About 40 springs in 10-acre area. Resort. Ref. 481.
7	Warm Springs, in secs. 19 and 20, T. 8 S., R. 13 E., on Warm Springs River 9 miles north-northeast of Warm Springs Indian Agency.	138–145	Large	Lake beds (Tertiary) overlying lava.		Many springs for 2 miles along river. Water smells of H₂S. Campground. Refs. 133, 483.
8	Lehman Hot Springs, in sec. 1, T. 5 S., R. 33 E., on Camas Creek.	Hot	75	Columbia River Basalt (Tertiary).		10 springs. Resort.
9	Hideaway Springs, in T. 5 S., R. 33 E., 7 miles southwest of Lehman Hot Springs (No. 8).	Hot		..do..		Several springs. Water smells of H₂S.
10	Sec. 6, T. 1 S., R. 39 E., 2 miles northeast of Summerville.	Warm		..do..		Several springs. Water used locally. Ref. 144.
11	Hot Lake, in T. 4 S., R. 39 E., 10 miles southeast of La Grande.	180	175	..do..		Water used for bathing.
12	Medical Springs, in sec. 24, T. 6 S., R. 41 E., 20 miles north-northeast of Baker.	140	50	Greenstone (Carboniferous).	482	2 springs. Water used locally.
13	Ritter (McDuffee) Hot Spring, sec. 8, T. 8 S., R. 30 E., on north bank of Middle Fork of John Day River.	110	35	Faulted Columbia River Basalt (Tertiary).		Resort. Refs. 109, 480.
14	Hot Sulphur Spring, in sec. 35, T. 10 S., R. 32 E., on Camp Creek 6 miles south of Susanville.	120		..do..		Resort. Refs. 144, 482.
15	Bear Gulch Spring, in sec. 11, T. 15 S., R. 31 E., near Canyon Creek 10 miles south of Canyon City.	Warm	2	Lava (upper Tertiary)		
16	Blue Mountain Hot Springs, in sec. 13, T. 14 S., R. 34 E., near mouth of Reynolds Creek 10 miles south of Prairie City.	Hot		Carboniferous strata		Several springs. Water used locally. Ref. 482.
17	Sam-O Mineral Springs, in sec. 2, T. 12 S., R. 43 E., 4 miles southeast of Durkee.	80		Faulted(?) Jurassic or Triassic strata.	481	2 springs. Water used locally. Ref. 482.
17A	Radium Hot Spring, in sec. 28, T. 7 S., R. 39 E., 10 miles northwest of Baker.	135	Small	Jointed diorite		Also 2 flowing wells. Water used for bathing.
17B	Sam-O Spring, in sec. 16, T. 9 S., R. 40 E., near Baker.	80	400	Alluvium overlying Tertiary volcanic and sedimentary rocks.		Water used for irrigation.
18	Belknap Hot Springs, in sec. 11, T. 16 S., R. 6 E., 6 miles east of McKenzie Bridge.	147–180	75	Conglomerate near lava (upper Tertiary).	133, 481	3 main springs. Water used for bathing. Resort. Refs. 137, 488.

No. on figure	Name or location	Temperature of water (°F)	Flow (gallons per minute)	Associated rocks	References on chemical quality	Remarks and additional references
				Oregon—Continued		
19	Foley Springs, in sec. 28, T. 16 S., R. 6 E., 4.5 miles southeast of McKenzie Bridge.	162–174	25	Columbia River Basalt (Tertiary).	137, 144	4 springs. Resort. Ref. 481.
20	Sec. 7, T. 17 S., R. 5 E., on the South Fork of McKenzie River, 8 miles southwest of McKenzie Bridge.	130 (max)	60	___do___		4 springs.
21	Wall Creek Hot Springs, in sec. 26, T. 20 S., R. 4 E., 10.5 miles northeast of Oakridge.	98	3	___do___		3 springs. Water used locally.
22	Winino (McCredie) Springs, in sec. 36, T. 21 S., R. 4 E., 11 miles east of Oakridge.	Hot	20	___do___		15 springs in 1-acre area. Resort.
23	Kitson Springs, in sec. 6, T. 22 S., R. 4 E., 8 miles southeast of Oakridge.	114	35	___do___		2 main springs. Resort.
24	Umpqua Warm Spring, in sec. 26, T. 26 S., R. 4 E., on Umpqua River 5 miles south of Potter Mountain.	105	5	Andesite (Tertiary)		2 springs.
25	Jackson (Bybee) Hot Springs, 2 miles northwest of Ashland.	104 (max)	70	Granite		8 springs. Resort.
25	Sec. 31, T. 24 S., R. 5½ E., in Summit Lake Valley.	Warm		Lava (Pliocene)		Several springs. Water used locally. Ref. 144.
27	Klamath Hot Springs, at Klamath Falls	185	150	___do___		Water used for bathing. Also several wells supplying hot water for heating of residences. Refs. 113, 150.
28	0.5 mile northeast of Olene	130	8	Lava (Tertiary)		Several springs. Water from one is used for domestic purposes.
28A	Taylor Warm Spring, 2 miles east of Olene	75	500	___do___		Water used for irrigation.
28B	Crystal Springs, 1 mile south of Olene	76	1,350	___do___		Water used for bathing and irrigation.
29	Oregon (Turner) Hot Springs, in sec. 10, T. 40 S., R. 13 E., 10 miles southeast of Bonanza.	148	35	Lake beds (Tertiary)		Water supply for sanitarium. Water used for bathing. Resort.
29A	Smith's Hot Spring, in sec. 10, T. 40 S., R. 13 E., 9.5 miles southeast of Bonanza.	146	5	___do___		Water used for bathing. Also water supply for cattle.
30	Wilkerson's Warm Springs, in sec. 6, T. 40 S., R. 14 E., 13 miles southeast of Bonanza.	76	20	Lava (Tertiary)		2 springs. Water used for domestic purposes and irrigation.
31	Robertson's Springs, in sec. 18, T. 38 S., R. 15 E., in Horsefly Valley 8 miles south of Bly.	Hot		Lava (upper Tertiary)		Several springs. Water used locally. Ref. 144.
32	Paulina Springs, in sec. 26, T. 21 S., R. 12 E., near north shore of Paulina Lake.	65; 70	10	Andesite and tuff (upper Tertiary).		2 springs. Ref. 487.
33	East Lake Hot Springs, in sec. 29, T. 21 S., R. 13 E., on south shore of East Lake.	110–141		Lake beds (Tertiary) near lava (Tertiary).		Many small springs. Water used for bathing. Ref. 487.
34	Sec. 36, T. 19 S., R. 32 E., near Twelve-mile Creek 20 miles southwest of Paulina.	60–87		___do___		Several springs. Water used locally. Ref. 487.
35	Sand Springs, in sec. 35, T. 25 S., R. 19 E., 5 miles northeast of Fossil Lake.	62	30	Alluvium overlying lake beds.		3 springs, of which the southernmost is called Mound Spring. Water supply for cattle. Ref. 490.
36	Sec. 32, T. 26 S., R. 18 E., on west shore of Christmas Lake.	62	3	___do___		Water used for domestic purposes. Ref. 490.
37	Ana River Springs, in sec. 6, T. 30 S., R. 17 E., 7 miles north of Summer Lake post office.	66	48,000–75,000	Lake beds overlying faulted basalt.	489	5 springs. Water supply for Summer Lake Irrigation District. Refs. 489, 490.
38	Buckhorn Creek Springs, in sec. 5, T. 30 S., R. 17 E., 9 miles north of Summer Lake Post Office.	68	1,000	___do___		Several springs. Water used for irrigation. Ref. 490.
39	Johnson Creek Springs, in sec. 34, T. 29 S., R. 17 E., 12 miles northeast of Summer Lake post office.	56	9,000	___do___		Do.
40	Thousand Springs, in sec. 19, T. 30 S., R. 18 E., on east side of Summer Lake Valley.	66	200	___do___		Many small springs. Water used for irrigation. Ref. 490.
40A	R. C. Foster's Spring, 2 miles southwest of Ana River.	66	2,500	___do___		Water used for irrigation. Ref. 489.
40B	W. O. Grisel's Spring	60.5	10	Faulted lake beds (Pliocene)		Water used for domestic purposes and irrigation. Ref. 489.
40C	Russell Emery's Spring	64.5	2	___do___		Water used for domestic purposes; also water supply for cattle. Ref. 489.
40D	J. G. Foster's Spring	65	50	___do___		5 springs. Water used for irrigation. Ref. 489.
40E	Lost Cabin Spring	67.5	100	___do___		Water supply for cattle. Ref. 489.
41	Pardon Warm Spring, in sec. 35, T. 30 S., R. 16 E.	76	40	Lake beds (Pliocene) near faulted lava.		Water used locally.
42	Summer Lake (Woodward; J. W. Farleigh's) Hot Spring, in sec. 11, T. 33 S., R. 17 E.	116	21	Lake beds (Pliocene)	489	3 main springs. Water smells of H_2S. Used for bathing and irrigation. Deposit of siliceous sinter. Ref. 490.
43	Sec. 12, T. 30 S., R. 22 E., on west shore of Alkali Lake.	59	25	Alluvium overlying lake beds (Pliocene).		Water used for domestic purposes; also water supply for cattle. Ref. 490.
44	Sec. 22, T. 32 S., R. 21 E., on XL Ranch 3 miles north of Abert Lake.	63	10	Lake beds (Pliocene) overlying basalt.		Water used for domestic purposes and irrigation. Ref. 490.
44A	Northeast shore of Abert Lake	65	20	Lake beds (Pliocene) near faulted lava (Tertiary).		Water supply for cattle.
44B	East shore of Abert Lake	68	10	___do___		Do.
44C	Southeast shore of Abert Lake	80	30	Lake beds (Pliocene)		Do.
44D	White Rock Ranch Springs, 10 miles north of Lakeview.	63; 71	10	Basalt (upper Tertiary)		2 springs. Water used for domestic purposes and irrigation.
44E	Russell Bean's Spring	69	Small	Alluvium		Water used for domestic purposes; also water supply for cattle. Ref. 489.
45	Hunters Hot Springs, 2 miles north of Lakeview.	128–162	600	Faulted lake beds (Pliocene)		12 main springs, also a flowing well 200 ft deep and discharging 120 gpm. Water from well used to heat hotel. Resort. Ref. 490.
46	Leo Hank's (Leithead, Joyland Plunge, Lakeview) Hot Spring, 1.5 miles south of Lakeview.	157	50	Faulted lava (Tertiary)	489	Water smells of H_2S. Used for bathing. Refs. 133, 144.

No. on figure	Name or location	Temperature of water (°F)	Flow (gallons per minute)	Associated rocks	References on chemical quality	Remarks and additional references
47	Gus Allen's (Barry Ranch, Down's, Lakeview) Hot Springs, 2 miles south of Lakeview.	175–185	50	Faulted lava (Tertiary)	489	3 springs. Water smells of H₂S. Used for irrigation.
47A	F. S. Longfellow's Spring	63	20	___do		Water used for domestic purposes and irrigation. Ref. 489.
48	Sec. 16, T. 35 S., R. 26 E., on upper Rock Creek 4 miles east of North Warner Lake.	105–115	50	Interbedded tuff and lava (Miocene).		Several springs. Water supply for cattle. Refs. 144, 491.
48A	Antelope Spring	104 Hot	30 Small	Faulted alluvium	489	Water used for bathing. Deposit of tufa.
49	Hart Mountain Hot Spring, in sec. 7, T. 36 S., R. 26 E., on the north side of Hart Mountain about 200 ft below crest.			Interbedded tuff and lava (Miocene).		Water supply for cattle.
49A	Fisher's Spring	144	20	Lake beds (Pliocene) near lava.		Water smells of H₂S. Used for bathing. Ref. 489.
49B	W. D. Moss Ranch, on west side of South Warner Lake.	72; 83	500; 30	Faulted lava (Tertiary)		2 main and several smaller springs. Water used for irrigation. Ref. 489.
49C	Charles Crump's Spring	104	5	Faulted lake beds (Tertiary)	489	Water smells of H₂S. Water supply for cattle. Deposit of tufa.
49D	Warner Valley Ranch	98; 107; 164	20; 2; 10	___do		3 springs. Deposit of siliceous sinter. Also a pool of sulfurous water. Ref. 489.
50	Adel Hot Spring, in sec. 23, T. 39 S., R. 24 E., 1 mile east of Adel post office.	160	10	___do		Water used locally.
50A	Pat Hallinan's Spring, 1 mile southwest of Houston Spring (No. 51).	1.3	20	Lake beds		4 springs. Water smells of H₂S. Water supply for cattle. Ref. 489.
51	Houston Hot Springs in sec. 27, T. 40 S., R. 24 E., 3 miles east of Warner Lake post office.	160	5	Faulted tuff and basalt		Water smells of H₂S. Used locally. Deposit of siliceous sinter. Ref. 489.
51A	Sec. 14, T. 22 S., R. 32½ E., 17 miles northeast of Burns.	72	225	Alluvium	486	Water contains 72 ppm of dissolved solids. Used for irrigation; also water supply for cattle.
52	Millpond Spring and other springs in secs. 35 and 36, T. 23 S., R. 30 E.	73–80	1,200	Interbedded tuff and basalt (Quaternary).	486	3 springs. Water contains 121 ppm of dissolved solids. Flow maintains log pond for saw mill. Refs. 371, 491.
52A	0.75 mile south of Millpond Spring (No. 52).	78	300	___do		Water used for irrigation; also water supply for cattle.
52B	Goodman Spring, 1 mile south of Millpond Spring (No. 52).	Warm	300	___do		Do.
52C	3.5 miles southwest of Millpond Spring (No. 52).	64	75	Lake beds, tuff, and rhyolite.		Water supply for cattle.
52D	1.5 miles east of spring No. 52C	72	485	___do		Water contains 113 ppm of dissolved solids. Used for irrigation; also water supply for cattle.
52E	Baker Spring, 1.5 miles southeast of spring No. 52D.	62–70	50	___do		5 springs. Water supply for cattle.
53	Crane Hot Spring, in sec. 34, T. 24 S., R. 33 E., near Crane Creek Gap 4 miles northwest of Crane.	122–126	180	Alluvium overlying lake beds (Pliocene).	486	2 main springs. Water contains 427 ppm of dissolved solids. Used for bathing. Refs. 371, 487, 491.
54	Sec. 23, T. 22 S., R. 36 E., on the west side of Middle Fork of Malheur River 8 miles northwest of Riverside.	138–144	90	Faulted interbedded tuff and basalt.		Several springs. Water used for bathing and irrigation. Ref. 491.
55	Sec. 16, T. 25 S., R. 36 E., on the west side of South Fork of Malheur River 8 miles north of Venator.	104–108	300	Faulted(?) lava (upper Tertiary).		Several springs. Water used for irrigation. Ref. 491.
56	Sec. 12, T. 26 S., R. 27 E., near south shore of Silver Lake.	68	45	Alluvium		Water used for irrigation. Ref. 491.
57	Sec. 33, T. 26 S., R. 28 E., 3.5 miles east of Iron Mountain.	68	10	___do		Water supply for cattle. Ref. 491.
58	Double-O Spring, in sec. 34, T. 26 S., R. 28 E., 1.5 miles west of Double-O Ranch.	74	5,350	Interbedded tuff, rhyolite, and lake beds (Pliocene).		Water used for irrigation; also water supply for cattle. Refs. 141, 486, 491.
59	Double-O Barnyard Spring, in sec. 33, T. 26 S., R. 28 E., on Double-O Ranch.	72	1,750	___do		Water used for irrigation; also water supply for cattle. Ref. 486.
60	Basque (East Double-O) Springs, in sec. 31, T. 26 S., R. 29 E., 1 mile southeast of Double-O Ranch.	67–74	1,800	___do	486	Several springs. Water used for irrigation; also water supply for cattle. Ref. 491.
61	Johnson Springs, in sec. 5, T. 27 S., R. 29 E., 2.5 miles southeast of Double-O Ranch.	72	900	___do		Several springs. Water used for irrigation; also water supply for cattle. Refs. 486, 491.
62	Hughet (Crane Creek) Spring, in sec. 8, T. 27 S., R. 29 E., 3 miles southeast of Double-O Ranch.	68	5,900	___do		Water used for irrigation; also water supply for cattle. Refs. 141, 486, 491.
62A	Sizemore Upper Spring, in sec. 9, T. 27 S., R. 29 E., 5 miles southeast of Double-O Ranch.	67	1,160	___do		Water used for irrigation; also water supply for cattle. Ref. 486.
62B	Sizemore Lower Spring, in sec. 15, T. 27 S., R. 29 E., 0.5 mile southeast of Sizemore Upper Spring (No. 62A).	66	410	___do		Do.
62C	Hurlburt Spring, in sec. 15, T. 27 S., R. 29 E., 1 mile southeast of Sizemore Lower Spring (No. 62B).	Warm	25	Alluvium		Water supply for cattle. Ref. 486.
62D	Between high- and low-water boundaries of Harney Lake.	66–108	30	___do		Several springs in southern and eastern parts of lake. Ref. 486.
63	Lynch Spring, in sec. 8, T. 27 S., R. 30 E.	65	25	___do		Water smells of H₂S. Ref. 486.
63A	Dunn Spring, in sec. 4, T. 27 S., R. 30 E., on south side of Mud Lake.	65; 70	10; 25	___do		2 springs 0.5 mile apart. Water supply for cattle. Ref. 486.
64	Sec. 36, T. 27 S., R. 29½ E., 0.5 mile from southeast shore of Harney Lake.	154	180	Lake beds, tuff, and rhyolite (Pliocene).	486	Refs. 371, 491.
64A	Sodhouse (Springer) Spring	54	1,800–5,200	Lake beds and playa deposits.		Water contains 226 ppm of dissolved solids. Used for irrigation; also water supply for cattle. Refs. 486, 491.
65	Hoghouse Spring, in sec. 13, T. 31 S., R. 32 E., on west side of Donner and Blitzen River valley.	78–80	1,800	Alluvium near faulted basalt (Tertiary).		Water used for irrigation. Refs. 486, 491.
66	Sec. 5, T. 32 S., R. 32½ E., 1 mile northeast of P Ranch.	83	100	___do		Water supply for cattle. Refs. 486, 491.
67	Sec. 12, T. 32 S., R. 32 E., 1 mile southwest of P Ranch.	89	500	___do		Water used for irrigation. Refs. 486, 491.

No. on figure	Name or location	Temperature of water (°F)	Flow (gallons per minute)	Associated rocks	References on chemical quality	Remarks and additional references
				Oregon—Continued		
68	Sec. 33, T. 34 S., R. 34 E., on west border of the Alvord Desert 6 miles south of Alvord Ranch.	168–177	135	Faulted lava (lower Tertiary).	------------------	Several springs. Water used locally. Refs. 144, 491.
69	Sec. 15, T. 37 S., R. 33 E., 2 miles south of Alvord Lake.	160	6	Lake beds (Pleistocene) near fault zone.	------------------	Several springs. Ref. 491.
70	Sec. 15, T. 37 S., R. 33 E., at old borax works 2.5 miles south of Alvord Lake.	97	900	Lake beds (Pleistocene)-----	------------------	Several springs. Water supply for abandoned borax works. Ref. 491.
71	Sec. 24, T. 38 S., R. 37 E., 5 miles northeast of Flagstaff Butte.	96–100	30	Interbedded tuffs and lava (Miocene).	------------------	4 springs. Water supply for cattle. Ref. 491.
71A	5 miles southwest of Whitehorse Ranch---	114	10	-----do-----	------------------	Water used for bathing.
72	Sec. 16, T. 39 S., R. 37 E., on north side of Trout Creek 0.5 mile downstream from mouth of Little Trout Creek.	128	45	-----do-----	------------------	Several springs. Water supply for cattle. Ref. 491.
73	Sec. 4, T. 16 S., R. 43 E., near Willow Creek 20 miles northwest of Vale.	Hot	----------	Payette Formation (Miocene and Pliocene?).	------------------	Also a nearby drilled well. Ref. 492.
74	Sec. 11, T. 19 S., R. 37 E., in Warm Creek valley near Beulah.	185	Small	-----do-----	------------------	Several springs. Water used locally. Ref. 371.
75	Neal Hot Spring, sec. 9, T. 18 S., R. 43 E., 12 miles northwest of Vale.	168	24	Faulted(?) Payette Formation (Miocene and Pliocene?).	------------------	Water used locally. Also a small warm spring nearby. Refs. 371, 492.
76	Sec. 18, T. 19 S., R. 43 E., on the Malheur River 15 miles southwest of Vale.	Hot	----------	Payette Formation (Miocene and Pliocene?) near lava.	------------------	Several springs. Ref. 492.
77	Vale Hot Springs, in sec. 20, T. 18 S., R. 45 E., on the south side of the Malheur River 0.5 mile east of Vale.	198	20	Payette Formation (Miocene and Pliocene?).	------------------	Also a nearby well 140 ft deep. Water used for bathing. Resort. Ref. 371.
78	Sec. 31, T. 17 S., R. 47 E., on the Malheur River 3 miles west of Ontario.	164	----------	-----do-----	------------------	Water used locally. Refs. 144, 667.
79	Mitchell Butte Hot Springs, in sec. 12, T. 21 S., R. 45 E., on the Owyhee River.	122–141	----------	-----do-----	------------------	3 main springs. Water used locally. Ref. 492.
80	Deer Butte Hot Spring, in sec. 14, T. 21 S., R. 45 E., on the Owyhee River.	115	----------	Interbedded tuff and lava---	------------------	Water used locally. Refs. 371, 492.
81	North Black Willow Spring, in sec. 25, T. 21 S., R. 45 E., on the Owyhee River near Sniveley's Ranch.	67	----------	Faulted Payette Formation (Miocene and Pliocene?).	------------------	Water used locally.
82	South Black Willow Spring, in sec. 35, T. 21 S., R. 45 E., on the Owyhee River.	71	----------	-----do-----	------------------	Water used locally. Ref. 492.
83	Sec. 10, T. 23 S., R. 44 E., on the Owyhee River 2 miles downstream from mouth of Dry Creek.	Hot	----------	Alluvium overlying lava (upper Tertiary).	------------------	Several springs. Ref. 492.
84	Sec. 20, T. 24 S., R. 37 E., near South Fork of Malheur River 5 miles south of Riverside.	106–143	60	Faulted(?) lava (upper Tertiary).	------------------	Several springs. Water used for irrigation. Ref. 491.
84A	Sec. 18, T. 27 S., R. 43 E., on the Owyhee River 30 miles northwest of Jordan Valley.	Hot	Large	-----do-----	------------------	
84B	Near north end of Saddle Mountain 25 miles northwest of Rome.	Warm	Small	-----do-----	------------------	
85	Canter's Hot Springs, in sec. 2, T. 30 S., R. 46 E., 0.5 mile west of Jordan Valley.	120	10	Lava (lower Tertiary)------	------------------	3 main springs. Water used for bathing. Ref. 144.
85A	Scott's Springs, 6 miles southwest of Rome.	68	5,000	Basalt (Tertiary)----------	------------------	Several springs. Water used for irrigation. Do.
85B	Tudor's Springs, 24 miles southwest of Rome.	68	6,000	-----do-----	------------------	
85C	South Fork of Owyhee River, 40 miles south of Jordan Valley.	88–95	1,000	Basalt overlying rhyolite (Tertiary).	------------------	About 15 springs within a distance of 0.5 mile.
86	Sec. 36, T. 40 S., R. 42 E., 6 miles north of McDermitt, Nev.	130	200	Faulted lava (Tertiary)-----	------------------	Several springs. Water used for irrigation. Ref. 144.

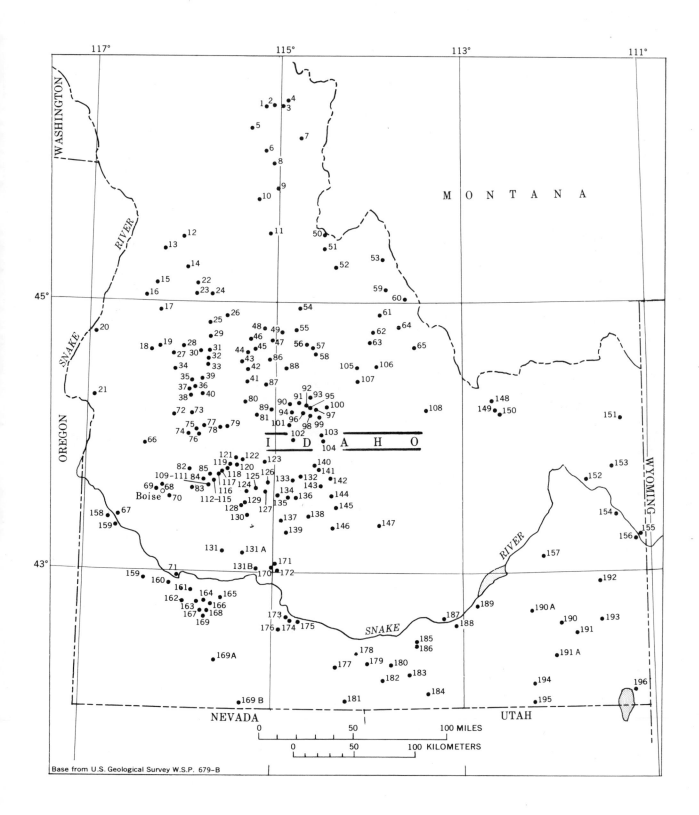

Idaho

1	Wier Creek Hot Springs, in sec. 13, T. 36 N., R. 11 E.	Hot	5	Granite		6 springs.
2	Colgate Springs, in sec. 9, T. 36 N., R. 12 E.	105–120	20	____do____		Do.
3	Jerry Johnson's Hot Springs, in sec. 7, T. 36 N., R. 13 E.	100–130	450	____do____		3 springs. Water used for bathing. Ref. 383.
4	Horse Creek, 4 miles southeast of Jerry Johnson's Hot Springs.	80	200	____do____		Ref. 383.
5	Stanley Hot Spring, in sec. 6, T. 34 N., R. 10 E., near Boulder Creek 4 miles upstream from junction with Lochsa River.	Hot	2	____do____		
6	Stuart Hot Spring, in sec. 4, T. 32 N., R. 11 E., on Link Creek 5 miles upstream from junction with Selway River.	Hot	35	____do____		
7	Sec. 4, T. 33 N., R. 14 E., 11 miles southwest of Elk Summit ranger station.	Warm	40	____do____		2 springs.
8	Martin Creek Hot Springs, in sec. 25, T. 31 N., R. 11 E., 3.5 miles west of Wylies Peak.	Hot	15	____do____		6 springs and seeps.
9	Sec. 14, T. 29 N., R. 12 E., 2 miles south of Grouse Peak.	Hot	10	____do____		
10	Red River Hot Springs, in sec. 10, T. 28 N., R. 10 E., 10 miles northeast of Red River ranger station.	120	15	____do____		4 springs. Resort. Ref. 383.
11	Barht's Hot Springs, in sec. 13, T. 25 N., R. 11 E., on Salmon River 200 yds below mouth of Hot Springs Creek.	Hot	200	____do____		Several springs. Water used locally.
12	Sec. 7, T. 24 N., R. 4 E., 2 miles north of Salmon River.	110	10	____do____		Water used for bathing.
13	Riggins Hot Spring, in sec. 13, T. 24 N., R. 2 E., 10 miles east of Riggins.	Hot		____do____		Water used locally.
14	Burgdorf Hot Spring, in sec. 1, T. 22 N., R. 4 E.	113	150	____do____		Resort.
15	Sec. 13, T. 21 N., R. 1 E., on east side of Little Salmon River 3 miles north of Round Valley.	Hot		____do____		Water smells of H_2S.

No. on figure	Name or location	Temperature of water (°F)	Flow (gallons per minute)	Associated rocks	References on chemical quality	Remarks and additional references
16	Yoghann Hot Sulphur Spring, in sec. 26, T. 20 N., R. 1 E., on west side of Little Salmon River 10 miles northwest of Meadows.	Hot	----------	Columbia River Basalt (Tertiary).	----------------	
17	Sec. 22, T. 19 N., R. 2 E., 3 miles northeast of Meadows.	100	50	Granite_____		Water used for bathing.
18	Sec. 2, T. 15 N., R. 1 E., 1.25 miles north of mouth of Warm Spring Creek.	Hot	100	_____do_____		6 springs.
19	Sec. 33, T. 16 N., R. 2 E., 15 miles east of Cottonwood.	Hot	25	_____do_____		8 springs.
20	T. 17 N., R. 5 W., in Snake River Canyon upstream from mouth of Brownlee Creek.	Hot	----------	Columbia River Basalt (Tertiary).		Water smells of H_2S. Ref. 482.
21	T. 11 N., R. 5 W., on Monroe Creek 6 miles northeast of Weiser.	Warm	----------	Payette Formation (Tertiary).		Several springs. Ref. 492.
22	Sec. 11, T. 21 N., R. 5 E., 12 miles west of Shiefers.	Hot	100	Granite_____		10 springs. Water smells of H_2S. Ref. 483.
23	Sec. 15, T. 20 N., R. 5 E., 15 miles southwest of Shiefers.	Warm	5	_____do_____		
24	Sec. 35, T. 20 N., R 7 E., on South Fork of Salmon River 7 miles south of Shiefers.	90–136	100	_____do_____		About 25 springs in 40-acre area.
25	Sec. 25, T. 18 N., R. 6 E., on South Fork of Salmon River 25 miles north of Knox.	Hot	15	_____do_____		10 springs.
26	Sec. 17, T. 18 N., R. 8 E., near mouth of Riordan Creek.	90	2	_____do_____		
27	T. 15 N., R. 3 E., 10 miles north of Cascade.	Hot	----------	_____do_____		Several springs.
28	T. 16 N., R. 4E., on Gold Fork River 25 miles north of Cascade.	Hot	----------	_____do_____		Do.
29	Sec. 1, T. 16 N., R. 6 E., on South Fork of Salmon River 15 miles north of Knox.	Hot	2	_____do_____		2 springs.
30	Sec. 17, T. 15 N., R. 6 E., 6 miles north of Knox.	Hot	100	_____do_____		
31	Sec. 14, T. 15 N., R. 6 E., 6 miles northeast of Knox.	Hot	250	_____do_____		2 springs, 0.5 mile apart.
32	Sec. 11, T. 14 N., R. 6 E., 4 miles east of Knox.	Hot	450	_____do_____		6 springs.
33	Sec. 14, T. 14 N., R. 6 E., 4 miles southeast of Knox.	Hot	100	_____do_____		
34	T. 14 N., R. 3 E., 0.25 mile from Cascade.	Hot	20	_____do_____		2 springs, 0.25 mile north and 0.25 mile south of Cascade. Water supply for town.
35	Sec. 2, T. 12 N., R. 5 E., on Middle Fork of Payette River 12 miles east of Alpha.	Hot	35	_____do_____		
36	Sec. 11, T. 12 N., R. 5 E., near Middle Fork of Payette River.	100	15	_____do_____		
37	Sec. 15, T. 12 N., R. 5 E., near Middle Fork of Payette River.	90	15	_____do_____		
38	Boiling Springs, in sec. 22, T. 12 N., R. 5 E., near Middle Fork of Payette River.	Hot	150	Faulted granite_____		18 springs. Water supply for Forest Service station.
39	Sec. 28, R. 13 N., R. 6 E., near Bull Creek 15 miles east of Alpha.	Hot	15	Granite_____		3 springs.
40	Sec. 31, T. 12 N., R. 6 E., near Silver Creek 15 miles southeast of Alpha.	90	250	_____do_____		4 springs.
41	Sec. 23, T. 13 N., R. 10 E., 0.5 mile southwest of mouth of Bear Valley Creek.	Hot	10	_____do_____		
42	Sec. 30, T. 14 N., R. 10E., 0.25 mile from mouth of Dagger Creek.	Warm	2	_____do_____		
43	Sec. 13, T. 14 N., R. 9 E., on Sulphur Creek.	80–110	7	_____do_____		3 springs.
44	Sec. 34, T. 15 N., R. 10 E., near mouth of Sulphur Creek.	Hot	25	_____do_____		Do.
45	Sec. 26, T. 15 N., R. 10 E., near Middle Fork of Salmon River.	Hot	3	_____do_____		2 springs.
46	Sec. 17, T. 16 N., R. 10 E., on branch of Indian Creek near Chinook Mountain.	Hot	10	Lava (Tertiary) overlying granite.	----------------	4 springs.
47	Sec. 20, T. 16 N., R. 12 E., 10 miles north of Greyhound.	Hot	40	Granite_____		2 springs.
48	Sec. 15, T. 17 N., R. 11 E., 8 miles south of Roosevelt.	Hot	50	Lava (Tertiary) overlying granite.		10 springs.
49	Sec. 28, T. 17 N., R. 13 E., on Middle Fork of Salmon River, 2 miles upstream from mouth of White Creek.	Hot	10	_____do_____		3 springs.
50	Sec. 17, T. 25 N., R. 17 E., on Horse Creek 25 miles northwest of Shoup.	110	10	Granite_____		Ref. 383.
51	Sec. 32, T. 24 N., R. 17 E., 17 miles west of Shoup.	Warm	25	_____do_____		5 springs.
52	T. 22 N., R. 18 E., on west side of Copper King Mountain.	Hot	----------	_____do_____		
53	Sec. 22, T. 23 N., R. 22 E., 5 miles north of Carmen.	Hot	80	_____do_____		14 springs.
54	Sec. 26, T. 19 N., R. 14 E., 1 mile east of Mormon Ranch.	Hot	40	_____do_____		
55	Sec. 19, T. 17 N., R. 14 E., near Cache Creek 4 miles upstream from its mouth.	Warm	10	_____do_____		
56	Sec. 10, T. 15 N., R. 14 E., on Warm Spring Creek.	80–190	400	Lava (Tertiary)_____		9 springs.
57	Sec. 1, T. 15 N., R. 15 E., 5 miles northwest of Parker Mountain.	Warm	75	_____do_____		4 springs.
58	Sec. 16, T. 15 N., R. 16 E., near Parker Mountain.	Hot	200	_____do_____		7 springs.
59	Salmon Hot Springs, in sec. 3, T. 20 N., R. 22 E., 7 miles south of Salmon.	Warm	400	Altered lava (Tertiary)_____		Several springs. Water used for bathing and irrigation.
60	Sec. 34, T. 20 N., R. 24 E., 7 miles northeast of Tendoy.	Hot	200	Belt Series (Precambrian)___		
61	T. 18 N., R. 22 E., 27 miles south of Salmon.	Hot	200	_____do_____		2 springs.
62	T. 17 N., R. 21 E., in Kronk Canyon of Salmon River 40 miles south of Salmon.	Hot	100	Belt Series (Precambrian)___	----------------	

No. on figure	Name or location	Temperature of water (°F)	Flow (gallons per minute)	Associated rocks	References on chemical quality	Remarks and additional references
63	Sec. 18, T. 16 N., R. 21 E., at upper end of Kronk Canyon of Salmon River 3 miles downstream from mouth of Pahsimeroi River.	Hot	100	Belt Series (Precambrian)		6 springs.
64	Warm Spring Creek, 4 miles southwest of Lemhi Indian Agency.	Warm		Lava (Tertiary) overlying Precambrian strata.		Several springs. Ref. 144.
65	Sec. 4, T. 15 N., R. 25 E., 10 miles west of Leadore.	87	3	Belt Series (Precambrian)		Water used for bathing.
66	Sec. 9, T. 7 N., R. 1 E., 1 mile southwest of Sweet.	Hot		Lava (Tertiary) overlying granite.		
67	T. 1 N., R. 3 W., on east side of Snake River 1 mile east of Enterprise.	67		Payette Formation (Tertiary).		Refs. 364, 371.
68	T. 4 N., R. 2 E., on west bank of Squaw Creek 3 miles north of Boise.	Hot	Large	...do...		Water used locally. Ref. 363.
69	T. 3 N., R. 2 E., on Cottonwood Creek 1 mile west of Boise.	Warm		...do...		Do.
70	Boise Hot Springs, in T. 3 N., R. 2 E., 4.5 miles southeast of Boise.	90–140	255	Faulted Payette Formation (Tertiary).		About 16 springs. Resort. Refs. 113, 150, 363, 370, 371.
71	Sec. 29, T. 5 S., R. 4 E., near Grand View	109	100	Faulted lava (Quaternary)		Water used for irrigation.
72	Sec. 20, T. 10 N., R. 3 E., 14 miles north of McNish ranger station.	Warm	30	Granite		
73	Sec. 32, T. 10 N., R. 4 E., 3 miles northwest of Garden Valley.	Hot		...do...		
74	Sec. 6, T. 8 N., R. 5 E., on South Fork of Payette River 10 miles east of Garden Valley.	Hot	20	...do...		2 springs. Campground.
75	Sec. 2, T. 8 N., R. 5 E., 0.5 mile west of Danskin Creek.	Hot	8	...do...		
76	Sec. 11, T. 8 N., R. 5 E., 1.5 miles east of Boston & Idaho power plant.	Hot	15	...do...		2 springs. Water used locally.
77	Sec. 31, T. 9 N., R. 6 E., 0.25 mile west of Pine Flat.	Hot	30	...do...		Campground.
78	Sec. 31, T. 9 N., R. 8 E., on north side of South Fork of Payette River.	Warm	40	...do...		
79	Kirkham Hot Springs, in sec. 32, T. 9 N., R. 8 E., on South Fork of Payette River.	90	150	...do...		5 springs.
80	Bonneville Hot Sprints, in sec. 31, T. 10 N., R. 10 E., on Warm Spring Creek.	100	200	...do...		6 springs.
81	Sacajawea Hot Springs, in sec. 30, T. 10 N., R. 11 E., near mouth of Bear Creek.	100	200	...do...		3 springs.
82	T. 5 N., R. 5 E., 6 miles southwest of Idaho City.	110–115	900	...do...		6 springs. Water used locally. Refs. 133, 144.
83	Nevin Spring, sec. 1, T. 3 N., R. 5 E., near mouth of Cottonwood Creek.	Hot	200	...do...		
84	Twin Springs, on north side of Middle Fork of Boise River downstream from mouth of Browns Creek.	Hot	350	...do...		2 main and several smaller springs.
85	Bassett Hot Spring, upstream from Logging Gulch, on north side of Middle Fork of Boise River.	Hot	30	...do...		
86	Sec. 1, T. 14 N., R. 11 E., 2 miles northwest of Greyhound.	Warm	4	...do...		
87	Sec. 2, T. 12 N., R. 13 E., 6 miles east of Cape Horn.	Warm	200	...do...		
88	Sec. 33, T. 14 N., R. 13 E., 10 miles southwest of Casto.	Warm	3	...do...		
89	Sec. 15, T. 10 N., R. 12 E., near Stanley	Hot	200	...do...		2 springs.
90	Sec. 36, T. 11 N., R. 13 E., near mouth of Yankee Fork of Salmon River.	Hot	250	...do...		5 springs.
91	Sec. 20, T. 11 N., R. 14 E., 4 miles east of mouth of Yankee Fork of Salmon River.	Hot	200	...do...		10 springs.
92	Secs. 22 and 27, T. 11 N., R. 14 E., 6 miles east of mouth of Yankee Fork of Salmon River.	Warm	5	...do...		
93	Sec. 19, T. 11 N., R. 15 E., on Salmon River 1 mile upstream from Sunbeam Dam.	168	200	...do...		6 springs.
94	Sec. 3, T. 10 N., R. 13 E., 2 miles south of mouth of Yankee Fork of Salmon River.	Warm	400	...do...		5 springs.
95	Robinson Bar Ranch Hot Springs, in sec. 34, T. 11 N., R. 15 E., at mouth of Warm Spring Creek.	130	40	...do...		3 springs. Resort. Also other springs along Warm Spring Creek.
96	T. 10 N., R. 15 E., near mouth of Hot Creek.	134–147		Limestone (Carboniferous)		Several springs along line 0.5 mile long.
97	Loon Creek Hot Springs, in T. 11 N., R. 15 E.	115–136	700	Faulted greenstone		20 springs. Water smells strongly of H_2S.
98	T. 10 N., R. 15 E., near head of Loon Creek	Hot		Granite		Several springs.
99	Sec. 19, T. 10 N., R. 16 E., on Slate Creek 6 miles upstream from its mouth.	Hot	200	Lava (Tertiary) overlying slate (Carboniferous).		10 springs in 2-acre area.
100	Sullivan Hot Springs, in sec. 27, T. 11 N., R. 17 E., on Sullivan Creek 3 miles west of Clayton.	107	5,000	Contact of lava (Tertiary) with limestone (Carboniferous).		Water used locally. Smells strongly of H_2S.
101	Sec. 18, T. 9 N., R. 14 E., on the Salmon River.	105	150	Granite		
102	Pierson Hot Spring, in sec. 27, T. 8 N., R. 14 E.	120	300	...do...		Resort. Ref. 375.
103	Secs. 30 and 31, T. 8 N., R. 17 E., on East Fork of Salmon River.	70–120	450	Limestone (Carboniferous) near lava.		8 springs.
104	Sec. 6, T. 7 N., R. 17 E., on East Fork of Salmon River.	75–110	300	...do...		6 springs.
105	Beardsley Hot Springs, in sec. 23, T. 14 N., R. 19 E., on east bank of Salmon River.	123 (max)	1,500	Faulted limestone and quartzite (Paleozoic).		Several springs. Resort.
106	Sulphur Creek Spring, in sec. 26, T. 14 N., R. 21 E., 15 miles northwest of Goldberg.	57	1,500	Paleozoic strata	365	Water used for irrigation.

Idaho—Continued

No. on figure	Name or location	Temperature of water (°F)	Flow (gallons per minute)	Associated rocks	References on chemical quality	Remarks and additional references
107	T. 13 N., R. 20 E., on Warm Springs Creek 10 miles southeast of Challis.	Warm	100	Basalt (Tertiary)		Several springs.
108	T. 9 N., R. 27 E., in Little Lost River Valley.	80		Paleozoic strata		Ref. 365.
109	South side of Middle Fork of Boise River, 0.25 mile downstream from mouth of Sheep Creek.	Hot	200	Granite		
110	Sheep Creek Bridge Spring, on Middle Fork of Boise River at Sheep Creek Bridge.	Hot	100	___do___		
111	Reed Spring, on Sheep Creek near its mouth.	Hot		___do___		
112	Smith Cabin Springs, on both sides of Middle Fork of Boise River upstream from junction with North Fork.	Hot	900	___do___		Several springs in 2-acre area.
113	Loftus Spring, on north side of Middle Fork of Boise River downstream from mouth of Loftus Creek.	Hot	100	___do___		
114	Crevice Spring, on north side of Middle Fork of Boise River downstream from mouth of Vaughn Creek.	Hot	20	___do___		
115	Vaughn Spring, on south side of Middle Fork of Boise River upstream from mouth of Vaughn Creek.	Hot	200			
116	Ninemeyer Springs, on south side of Middle Fork of Boise River downstream from mouth of Big Five Creek.	Hot	900	___do___		10 springs.
117	Pool Creek Spring, on north side of Middle Fork of Boise River upstream from mouth of Pool Creek.	Warm	50	___do___		
118	South side of Middle Fork of Boise River upstream from mouth of Straight Creek.	Hot	180	___do___		
119	Dutch Frank's Springs, on south side of Middle Fork of Boise River downstream from mouth of Dutch Frank's Creek.	Hot	1,800	___do___		Many springs in 3-acre area.
120	Granite Creek Springs, on Middle Fork of Boise River, in sec. 4, T. 5 N., R. 9 E., 8 miles east of Narton.	130 (max)	50	___do___		7 springs.
121	T. 5 N., R. 9 E., on both sides of Middle Fork of Boise River, 0.25 mile upstream from mouth of Granite Creek.	Hot	200	___do___		About 40 springs in 2-acre area.
122	Sec. 36, T. 6 N., R. 9 E., on south side of Middle Fork of Boise River, 0.5 mile downstream from mouth of Granite Creek.	130 (max)	30			Several springs in 1-acre area. Water used for bathing.
123	Sec. 32, T. 6 N., R. 12 E., 2 miles east of Atlanta.	100–130	50	___do___		6 springs. Water used for bathing.
124	Sec. 10, T. 3 N., R. 10 E., 0.5 mile northeast of Featherville.	Warm	45	___do___		Water used for bathing.
125	Sec. 9, T. 3 N., R. 11 E., 7 miles east of Featherville.	Warm	Small	___do___		
126	Sec. 24, T. 4 N., R. 11 E., on Willow Creek, 10 miles northeast of Featherville.	Hot	45	___do___		Several springs.
127	Sec. 13, T. 3 N., R. 11 E., on South Fork of Boise River 10 miles east of Featherville.	Hot	30	___do___		4 springs.
128	Sec. 5, T. 2 N., R. 10 E., 6 miles south of Featherville.	Hot	50	___do___		12 springs in 5-acre area. Water used for bathing.
129	Sec. 33, T. 3 N., R. 10 E., 4.5 miles south of Featherville.	128	45	___do___		12 springs in 1 acre area. Water used for bathing. Campground.
130	Sec. 5, T. 1 N., R. 10 E., north of Fishing Falls.	164 (max)		___do___	144	Several springs. Water used locally. Ref. 138.
131	Hot (Ranch) Springs, in sec. 16, T. 3 S., R. 8 E., 10 miles east of Mountain Home.	103–167	900	Faulted lava		Several springs. Water used for bathing. Refs. 370, 371.
131A	Daugherty's (Lattie's) Hot Spring, 15 miles north of Glenns Ferry.	146	500	___do___		Water used for bathing and irrigation.
131B	Hot Spring, 1 mile east of King Hill.	125	20	___do___		Also a drilled well. Water used for bathing and irrigation.
132	Sec. 1, T. 4 N., R. 14 E., on Big Smoky Creek 8 miles north of Carrietown.	Warm	10	Granite		
133	Sec. 32, T. 4 N., R. 14 E., on Big Smoky Creek 8 miles northwest of Carrietown.	Hot	20	Granite		About 30 springs.
134	Sec. 18, T. 3 N., R. 13 E., on South Fork of Boise River near mouth of Bear Creek.	Warm	15	___do___		15 springs.
135	Sec. 30, T. 3 N., R. 14 E., on Little Smoky Creek 8 miles southwest of Carrietown.	Warm	10	___do___		Ref. 144.
136	Wasewick Hot Springs, in sec. 28, T. 3 N., R. 14 E., 6 miles southwest of Carrietown.	125–150	250	___do___		About 50 springs. Water used locally. Ref. 375.
137	Wardrop Hot Springs, in sec. 29, T. 1 N., R. 13 E., on Corral Creek 2 miles north of Corral.	Hot	100	Lava (Tertiary)		About 25 springs. Resort.
138	Sec. 14, T. 1 N., R. 15 E., 5 miles north of Blaine.	Warm	15	___do___		
139	Sec. 34, T. 1 S., R. 13 E., 5 miles south of Corral.	Hot	25	___do___		20 springs.
140	Russian John Hot Springs, in sec. 33, T. 6 N., R. 16 E., near Wood River 18 miles northwest of Ketchum.	102	50	Lava (Tertiary) overlying Paleozoic strata.		4 springs. Ref. 375.
141	Easly Warm Springs, in sec. 11, T. 5 N., R. 16 E., on south side of Wood River 16 miles northwest of Ketchum.	99	100	___do___		Do.
142	Guyer Hot Springs, in sec. 15, T. 4 N., R. 17 E., 2.5 miles west of Ketchem.	160	450	Faulted black limestone	376	Several springs. Resort. Deposit of tufa.

No. on figure	Name or location	Temperature of water (°F)	Flow (gallons per minute)	Associated rocks	References on chemical quality	Remarks and additional references
				Idaho—Continued		
143	Sec. 36, T. 4 N., R. 16 E., on Warm Spring Creek 11 miles southwest of Ketchum.	Hot	450	Lava (Tertiary) overlying Paleozoic strata.		6 springs. Water used for bathing. Ref. 144.
144	Clarendon Hot Springs, in sec. 26, T. 3 N., R. 17 E., on Deer Creek 6 miles west of Hailey.	125–150	100	Black limestone (Paleozoic).	376	3 springs. Water used for bathing.
145	Hailey Hot Springs, in sec. 18, T. 2 N., R. 18 E., 2.5 miles southwest of Hailey.	146	50	Slate (Paleozoic).	376	Several springs. Water piped to baths and hotel in Hailey.
146	Lava Creek Hot Spring, in sec. 24, T. 1 S., R. 17 E., near Magic Reservoir.	96	130	Snake River Group (Quaternary overlying rhyolite.)		
147	Condie Hot Springs, in sec. 14, T. 1 S., R. 21 E., near Carey.	124	450	....do............		2 springs. Water used for bathing and irrigation.
148	Sec. 25, T. 11 N., R. 32 E., 10 miles south of Edie.	80	3,000	Limestone (Carboniferous).		2 springs.
149	Sec. 34, T. 10 N., R. 33 E., 18 miles west of Dubois.	Hot	....	Lava (Tertiary) overlying limestone (Carboniferous).		
150	Lidy Hot Springs, in sec. 2, T. 9 N., R. 33 E., 16 miles west of Dubois.	124	300	Faulted rhyolite overlying carboniferous strata.		Several springs. Water used for bathing and irrigation.
151	Sec. 6, T. 9 N., R. 44 E., near Warm River.	Warm	50	Lava (Tertiary).		3 springs.
152	Heise Hot Spring, in sec. 25, T. 4 N., R. 40 E., on South Fork of Snake River at Heise.	120	400	Faulted lava.		Resort. Ref. 373.
153	Pincock (Lime Kiln) Hot Spring, in sec. 6, T. 5 N., R. 43 E., 6 miles south of Canyon City.	Hot	65	Limestone (Paleozoic).		Resort.
154	Sec. 29, T. 1 N., R. 43 E., on Fall Creek 4 miles northwest of Irwin.	Warm	....	Faulted Paleozoic strata.		Several springs. Water used locally. Ref. 373.
155	Alpine Hot Springs, in secs. 18 and 19, T. 2 S., R. 46 E., on east side of South Fork of Snake River 5 miles northwest of Alpine.	120–150	25	Limestone (Carboniferous).		2 main and several small springs. Water smells of H₂S. Deposit of tufa. Resort.
156	Secs. 13 and 24, T. 2 S., R. 45 E., on west side of South Fork of Snake River 3 miles southwest of Blowout.	88–144	....	Faulted limestone (Carboniferous).		6 springs. Water used for bathing. Refs. 372, 373, 667.
157	Lincoln Valley Warm Springs, in sec. 36, T. 3 S., R. 37 E., 3 miles south of old Fort Hall.	69–87	....	Limestone (Carboniferous?).		5 springs. Water used locally. Refs. 138, 144.
158	Enterprise, in T. 1 N., R. 3 W.	128	3,000	Payette Formation (Tertiary).		Water used for bathing and irrigation. Refs. 364, 371.
159	Given's Hot Springs, in T. 1 S., R. 3 W., on south side of Snake River near mouth of Reynolds Creek.	98	35	Miocene sediments near Tertiary lava.		2 springs. Water used for bathing. Refs. 133, 137, 144.
159A	Toy Ranch, in sec. 29, T. 5 S., R. 1 E.	115–120	50	Alluvium.		Several springs. Water used for bathing.
160	Sec. 14, T. 6 S., R. 3 E., on Shoofly Creek near Grand View.	Warm	300	Payette Formation (Tertiary).		2 springs. Water used for irrigation. Deposit of tufa.
161	Rosebrier Spring, in sec. 32, T. 6 S., R. 5 E., on Little Valley Creek 10 miles southeast of Comet.	68	Small	Alluvium near fault in Payette Formation (Tertiary).		Also a drilled well. Water used locally. Ref. 368.
162	Sec. 24, T. 7 S., R. 4 E., near head of Little Valley Creek.	99	135	Payette Formation (Tertiary).		Also 5 drilled wells. Water used for irrigation. Ref. 368.
163	Bruneau Hot Spring, in sec. 21, T. 7 S., R. 6 E., near Hot Springs post office on west side of Bruneau Valley.	105	1,200	....do............		Water used for bathing and irrigation. Refs. 368, 370, 371.
164	Sec. 22, T. 7 S., R. 6 E., in Bruneau Valley.	111	35	....do............		Water used locally. Ref. 368.
165	Trammel's Hot Springs, in sec. 22, T. 7 S., R. 6 E., in Bruneau Valley.	114	1,000	....do............		Several springs. Water used for bathing and irrigation. Ref. 368.
166	Sec. 35, T. 7 S., R. 6 E., on east bank of Bruneau River.	Warm	Large	....do............		Ref. 368.
167	Hot Creek Springs, in sec. 3, T. 8 S., R. 6 E., 11 miles south of Bruneau.	94–98.5	1,800	Basalt (Eocene) overlying tuff.		Several springs. Water used for irrigation. Ref. 368.
168	Sec. 3, T. 8 S., R. 6 E., downstream from mouth of Hot Creek.	100	....	Payette Formation (Tertiary).		Several springs. Water used locally. Ref. 368.
169	Sec. 29, T. 8 S., R. 7 E., 100 yd downstream from Buckaroo diversion dam in Bruneau Valley.	105	....	....do............		Ref. 368.
169A	Indian (Bat) Hot Springs, in sec. 33, T. 12 S., R. 7 E., on West Fork of Bruneau River.	145–158	2,000	Basalt (Tertiary) overlying rhyolite.		2 main springs in deep canyon. Water used for bathing. Refs. 148, 377.
169B	Kitty's Hot Hole, 10 miles southwest of Three Creek.	Hot	Small	Basalt (Tertiary).		Water used for bathing. Ref. 148.
170	White Arrow Hot Springs, in sec. 31, T. 4 S., R. 13 E., near Blanche.	149	1,200	Lava (Pliocene).		4 springs. Water used for bathing and irrigation.
171	Blanche Crater Warm Springs, 1.5 miles northeast of White Arrow Hot Springs (no. 170).	80	Small	Lava (Quaternary).		Maintains Soda (Lye) Lake having area of 3 acres.
172	Tschannen Warm Springs, 2 miles southeast of White Arrow Hot Springs (no. 170).	110	Small	Lava (Pliocene).		Nearby artesian well flows 200 gpm. Water used locally.
173	Sec. 30, T. 8 S., R. 14 E., on island in Salmon Falls Creek near Austin.	130	5	Lake beds (Tertiary) overlying lava.		Water used for bathing.
174	Ring's Hot Spring, in sec. 31, T. 8 S., R. 14 E., on south side of Snake River.	125	200	Faulted lake beds (Miocene).		Forms pool bubbling with odorless gas. Water used locally.
175	Banbury Hot Springs, in sec. 33, T. 8 S., R. 14 E., on south bank of Snake River 4 miles upstream from mouth of Salmon River.	131	600	....do............		2 springs and flowing drilled well. Ref. 370.
176	Poison Spring, in T. 9 S., R. 13 E., in canyon of Salmon River 8 miles upstream from mouth of river.	Warm	Small	Lava (Tertiary).		Ref. 370.
177	Sec 10, T. 13 S., R. 18 E., on Rock Creek 10 miles south of Stricker.	90	1,300	....do............		3 springs
178	Artesian City Hot Springs, in sec. 6, T. 12 S., R. 20 E.	100	Small	....do............		Also several flowing wells discharging 500 gpm. Water used for bathing and irrigation.

No. on figure	Name or location	Tempera-ture of water (°F)	Flow (gallons per minute)	Associated rocks	References on chemical quality	Remarks and additional references
				Idaho—Continued		
179	Poulton Warm Spring, in sec. 6, T. 13 S., R. 21 E., 9 miles northwest of Oakley.	72	----------	Limestone (Paleozoic)_____	367_____	Also flowing wells. Water used locally.
180	Land Spring, in sec. 7, T. 13 S., R. 23 E., 6 miles northeast of Oakley.	60	2,000	Faulted rhyolite (Tertiary) _	367_____	Water used for irrigation.
181	Thoroughbred Springs, in sec. 21, T. 16 S., R. 19 E.	69	200	Miocene strata overlying faulted Paleozoic strata.	------------------	Several springs. Water used locally. Ref. 367.
182	Oakley Warm Spring, in sec. 27, T. 14 S., R. 22 E., 5 miles south of Oakley.	114	10	Quartzite (Carboniferous?)__	367_____	Also flowing well. Water used locally.
183	Sec. 6, T. 14 S., R. 25 E., 1 mile southwest of Elba.	Warm	----------	Carboniferous strata_____	------------------	
184	Frazier Hot Spring, in sec. 23, T. 15 S., R. 26 E., 5 miles southwest of Bridge.	204	120	Alluvium near faulted Carboniferous strata.	------------------	Also well 400 ft deep. Water used for irrigation.
185	Bridger Hot Spring, in sec. 11, T. 11 S., R. 25 E., 6 miles northeast of Albion.	120	4	Faulted lake beds (Bridger Formation).	------------------	Also 3 flowing wells. Water supply for cattle.
186	Sec. 22, T. 11 S., R. 25 E., 4 miles northeast of Albion.	100	3	_____do_____	------------------	Water supply for cattle.
187	Sec. 19, T. 9 S., R. 28 E., near Lake Walcott.	70	700	_____do_____	------------------	5 springs.
188	Fall Creek Warm Springs, in sec. 29, T. 9 S., R. 29 E., 8 miles northeast of Yale.	62	9,000	Lake beds (Eocene) faulted against limestone (Carboniferous).		Several springs. Deposit of tufa.
189	Indian Hot Springs, in sec. 19, T. 8 S., R. 31 E., on south side of Snake River.	140	1,000	Faulted limestone (Paleozoic).	------------------	Several springs. Water used for bathing. Resort.
190	Lava Hot Springs, in T. 9 S., R. 38 E., on both sides of Portneuf River 2 miles south of Lava.	100–144	4,200	Faulted quartzite (Paleozoic).	------------------	Several springs. Water used for bathing. Resort. Ref. 374.
190A	6 miles northwest of McCammon_____	Warm	Small	Lava (Tertiary)_____	------------------	Water used for bathing.
191	T. 10 S., R. 40 E., on west side of Bear River at south end of Gentile Valley.	125	----------	Lava overlying Paleozoic strata.	362?_____	5 springs rising in pools. Ref. 144.
191A	Downata Hot Springs, 4 miles southeast of Downey.	112	470	Gravel (Quaternary)_____	------------------	Water used for bathing and irrigation.
192	T. 6 S., R. 42 E., in canyon of Blackfoot River.	82	Small	Limestone and shale (Carboniferous).	------------------	Deposit of tufa. Refs. 366, 374.
193	Bear River Soda (Beer) Springs, in T. 9 S., R. 42 E.	76–88	----------	Limestone (Carboniferous)__	------------------	Several springs, of which the main spring is Steamboat Spring. Resort. Refs. 366, 374, 413, 625, 666.
194	T. 14 S., R. 36 E., 2 miles southwest of Malad.	85	----------	Carboniferous strata_____	------------------	Several springs. Water used locally. Ref. 144.
195	T. 16 S., R. 36 E., 12 miles southeast of Malad.	Warm	----------	_____do_____	------------------	Do.
196	Bear Lake Hot Springs, near northeast shore of Bear Lake and 16 miles south of Montpelier.	83–134	150	_____do_____	------------------	3 springs. Resort. Ref. 124.

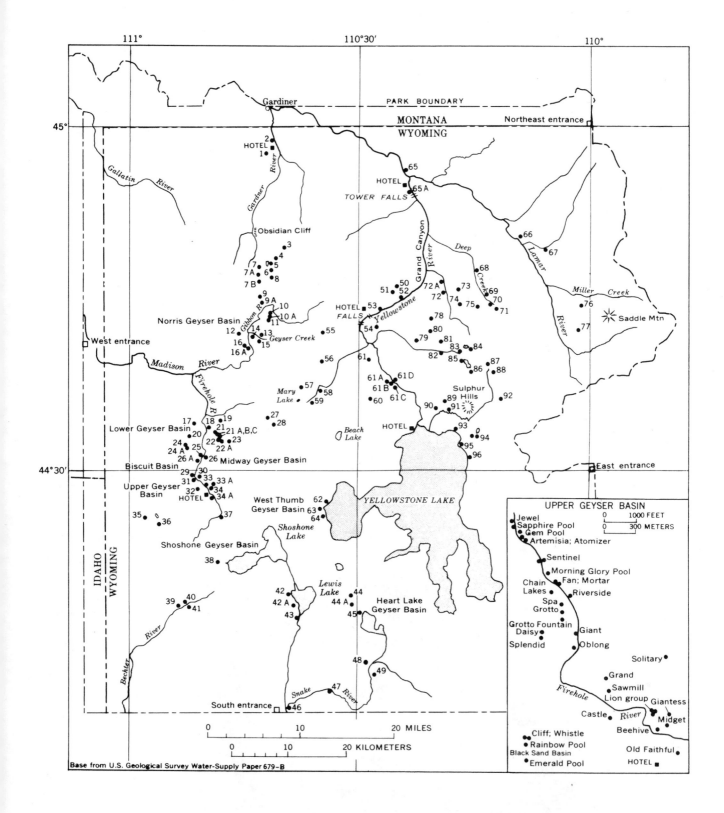

THERMAL SPRINGS OF YELLOWSTONE NATIONAL PARK, WYOMING

1	Boiling (Hot) River, 0.8 mile north-northeast of Yellowstone Park Headquarters.		10,000		562	Several springs, the flows combining to form stream, 6–8 ft wide, flowing into Gardiner River. Refs. 592, 625–628, 672.
2	Mammoth (White Mountain) Hot springs, 0.5 mile southwest of Yellowstone Park Headquarters.	160 (max)	225–1,152	Rhyolite overlying Mesozoic strata.	562	Several springs. Extensive deposits of travertine. Refs. 140, 557, 558, 574, 608, 617, 620, 625, 628, 634, 636, 637, 642, 645, 655, 664, 667, 679, 692, 697, 698.
3	3 miles east of Obsidian Cliff		Small	Rhyolite (Tertiary)		
4	Northeast base of The Landmark		Small	do		
5	Near east side of Lake of the Woods		Small	do		
6	0.5 mile southeast of Lake of the Woods		Small	do		
7	Amphitheater Springs, 0.8 mile west of Lake of the Woods.	135–196		do	562	Also solfataras.
7A	Clearwater Springs, 1 mile southwest of Amphitheater Springs (No. 7) and 0.5 mile northwest of Roaring Mountain.	178–198		Clay	562	Several boiling springs and fumaroles. Ref. 562.
7B	Pool in crater of Semi-Centennial Geyser, near Obsidian Creek 0.6 mile south of Clearwater Springs (No. 7A).	Hot		Rhyolite (Tertiary)		Erupted violently in August 1922, but ceased geyser action soon thereafter. Refs. 637, 667.
8	Whiterock Springs, 1 mile south-southeast of Lake of the Woods.	149–156	Small	do	562	2 springs. Ref. 561.
9	Bijah Spring, 0.4 mile northwest of Fryingpan Springs (No. 10).	184	58.5	do	562	Rises in large clear pool. Ref. 561.
9A	Fryingpan Springs, 2 miles northwest of Norris Junction.			do	562	Many bubbling vents on both sides of Mammoth-Norris Junction Road.
10	Congress Pool, 0.3 mile southwest of Norris Junction.			do		Muddy pool, sometimes boiling and sometimes quiescent.
10A	Crater of Monarch Geyser, near Congress Pool (No. 10).			do		Formerly erupted to height of 100–200 ft. Ceased activity in 1913. Ref. 637.
11	Geysers in Norris Geyser Basin:			do		
	Ebony Geyser			do		Erupts to height of 25–50 ft at intervals of 8–48 hr. Ref. 637.
	Echinus Geyser			do		Erupts to height of 75–100 ft at intervals of 1–1.5 hr. Ref. 637.
	Emerald Spring			do	562	Erupts occasionally to height of 20–30 ft. Ref. 637.
	Fan Geyser			do		Erupts to maximum height of 25 ft at intervals of 7–19 hr. Refs. 637, 647.
	Ledge Geyser			do		Erupts to height of 60–75 ft several times a day. Ref. 637.
	Mud Geyser			do		Erupts to height of 8–60 ft at intervals of 20 min. Ref. 637.
	Steamboat Geyser			do		Erupts to height of 25–30 ft at intervals of 2–5 min. Ref. 637.
	Valentine Geyser			do		Erupts to height of 60–75 ft at intervals of 18–72 hr. Ref. 637.
	100 ft northwest of Valentine Geyser			do		Erupts to height of 20–35 ft several times an hr. Ref. 637.
	Vixen Geyser			do		Erupts to height of 18–30 ft several times a day. Refs. 566, 637.
	Whirligig Geyser			do		Erupts to height of 8–15 ft once or twice a day. Refs. 576, 637.

No. on figure	Name or location	Temperature of water (°F)	Flow (gallons per minute)	Associated rocks	References on chemical quality	Remarks and additional references
						Wyoming—Continued
12	Sylvan Springs, in Gibbon Meadows 3.5 miles southwest of Norris Junction.	190 (max)	Small		562	Several springs and fumaroles; also large shallow pool. Ref. 561.
13	Gibbon Hill Geyser, near east side of Gibbon Meadows at foot of southwest side of Gibbon Hill.	188–198		Rhyolite (Tertiary)	562	Erupts to height of 15–25 ft several times a day. Ref. 637.
14	Artists Paintpots, at foot of northwest side of Paintpot Hill.	178–199	149	do	562	Pools of bubbling mud; also fumaroles. Ref. 576.
15	Geyser Springs, at foot of east side of Paintpot Hill.			do		Several springs including an unnamed geyser that erupts to height of 25 ft at intervals of 6 min. Ref. 637.
16	Monument Geyser in Monument Geyser Basin 1 mile west-southwest of Paintpot Hill.	197	5,400	do	562	Erupts to height of 4–9 ft almost constantly. Also several springs issuing from small cones. Barren area 240 yd long and 50 yd wide.
16A	Beryl Spring, 1.5 miles north of Gibbon Falls.	197	54	do	562	Pool 20 ft in diameter. Water in constant ebullition. Ref. 576.
17	Queen's Laundry (Red Terrace) Spring, 1.5 miles southwest of Fountain Ranger Station.	160		do	562	Large pool. Terraces of sinter. Ref. 561.
18	River Group Springs, on both sides of Firehole River 1.5 miles south of Fountain Ranger Station.	119–203		do	562	Numerous springs including 6 that are superheated and 3 small geysers. Ref. 561.
19	Morning Mist Springs, near Nez Perce Creek 1.2 miles east-southeast of Fountain Ranger Station.	201 (max)	Small	do		Numerous springs.
20	Fairy Springs, 2.7 miles south-southwest of Fountain Ranger Station.	184–202		do	562	4 groups of springs. Includes Boulder Springs, the water of which is in constant ebullition. Ref. 561.
21	Fountain Paintpot			Rhyolite (Tertiary)	562	Large cauldron of white, pink, and pale orange clay. Ref. 557.
21A	Clepsydra Geyser			do		Erupts to height of 5–25 ft at intervals of 3 min. Refs. 576, 637.
21B	Fountain Geyser, 2.2 miles southeast of Fountain Ranger Station.			do		Erupts to height of 50–75 ft at intervals of 6–12 hr. Refs. 557, 576, 637, 665.
21C	Morning Geyser, near Fountain Geyser (No. 21B).			do		Erupts to height of 50–60 ft at intervals of 2–5 days. Refs. 576, 637.
22	Great Fountain Geyser, 1 mile south-southeast of Fountain Geyser (No. 21B).	204	22	do	562	Erupts to maximum height of 90 ft at intervals of 8–15 hr. Large deposit of sinter. Refs. 557, 637.
22A	Pink Cone Geyser			do		Erupts to height of 12–17 ft once a day. Sinter cone is 18 in. high and 5 feet in diameter. Ref. 637.
23	White Dome Geyser, 0.8 mile south of Fountain Geyser (No. 21B).			do		Erupts to height of 18–30 ft at intervals of 20–30 min. Ref. 637.
24	Spray Geyser, at base of south end of Twin Buttes 4 miles southwest of Fountain Ranger Station.		72	do		Erupts to height of 5–20 ft at intervals of 2–31 min. Ref. 637.
24A	Pool in crater of Imperial Geyser, 0.2 mile west of Spray Geyser.		690	Rhyolite (Tertiary)	562	Began erupting in 1928 to height of 100–125 ft; ceased erupting in 1929. Ref. 637.
25	Prismatic Lake in crater of Excelsior Geyser, about midway between Upper Basin Ranger Station and Fountain Ranger Station.	146	2,700	do	562	Formerly the largest geyser in Yellowstone Park but dormant since 1888. Lake is 370 ft long and water is blue-green. Much steam. Turquoise and Opal Pools nearby, also several hot springs. Refs. 557, 576, 587, 611, 617, 637.
26	Flood Geyser, 0.5 mile southeast of Prismatic Lake (No. 25).	201	18	do	562	Erupts to height of several ft at irregular intervals. Ref. 637.
26A	Rabbit Creek area, 1 mile east-southeast of Prismatic Lake (No. 25).	201 (max)		do	562	Several springs and large pool of blue water; also paintpots and fumaroles. Ref. 637.
27	Tributary of Juniper Creek, 6.5 miles east of Fountain Ranger Station.			do		
28	Juniper Creek Springs, 1.1 miles southeast of No. 27.			do		
29	Biscuit Basin, 2.2 miles northwest of Old Faithful Inn:					
	Jewel Geyser	190		do	562	Erupts to height of 12–22 ft at intervals of 5–10 min. Ref. 637.
	Sapphire Pool (Soda Geyser)	201		do	562	Erupts to height of 4–12 ft at intervals of 10–20 min. Water is exceptionally clear. Ref. 637.
30	1.7 miles northwest of Old Faithful Inn, on northeast side of Firehole River:					
	Gem Pool			do		Water is clear and quiescent.
	Artemisia Geyser			do	562	Erupts to height of 15–35 ft at intervals of 24–30 hr. Ref. 637.
	Atomizer Geyser			do		Erupts to height of 20–40 ft once a day. Ref. 637.
30A	1.2 miles northwest of Old Faithful Inn, on northeast side of Firehole River:					
	Sentinel Geysers	201		do	562	2 geysers. Erupt to maximum height of 20 ft at intervals of 2–3 days. Ref. 637.
	Morning Glory Pool	171		do	562	Refs. 576, 677.
	Fan Geyser	198		do		Erupts to height of 6–100 ft two or three times a year. Refs. 637, 612.
	Mortar Geyser	198		do		Erupts to maximum height of 30 ft two or three times a year. Ref. 637.
	Riverside Geyser			do	562	Erupts obliquely to height of 80–100 ft at intervals of 6–9.5 hr. Refs. 637, 665.

No. on figure	Name or location	Temperature of water (°F)	Flow (gallons per minute)	Associated rocks	References on chemical quality	Remarks and additional references

No. on figure	Name or location	Temperature of water (°F)	Flow (gallons per minute)	Associated rocks	References on chemical quality	Remarks and additional references
31	1 mile northwest of Old Faithful Inn, on southwest side of Firehole River:					
	Chain Lakes (Bottomless Pit) Geyser			Rhyolite (Tertiary)		Erupts to height of 35–75 ft at intervals of 2–3 weeks. Refs. 566, 637.
	Spa Geyser			do		Erupts rarely to maximum height of 50 ft. Ref. 637.
	Grotto Geyser			do		Erupts to height of 20–30 ft at intervals of 2–8 hr. Refs. 576, 644, 647, 651, 655, 660, 661, 677, 689.
	Grotto Fountain			do		Erupts to maximum height of 65 ft at intervals of 6–12 hr. Ref. 637.
	Daisy Geyser	198		do	562	Erupts obliquely to maximum height of 75 ft at intervals of 1.5–3 hr. Ref. 637.
	Splendid Geyser	200		do	562	Erupts rarely to height of 125–150 ft. Ref. 637.
	Giant Geyser	205		do	562	Erupts to height of 150–180 ft at intervals of 6–16 days; sometimes inactive for long periods. Refs. 574, 579, 637, 648, 649, 652, 655, 665, 672, 679, 689.
	Oblong Geyser	202		do	562	Erupts to height of 20–40 ft at intervals of 5–8 hr. Ref. 637.
32	0.5 mile north-northwest of Old Faithful Inn, on northeast side of Firehole River:					
	Grand Geyser			do	562	Erupts to height of 180–200 ft at intervals of 8–80 hr. Refs. 579, 637, 652, 663, 672.
	Turban Geyser			do		Erupts to maximum height of 25 ft simultaneously with nearby Grand Geyser. Refs. 645, 663.
	Sawmill Geyser			do	562	Erupts to height of 17–32 ft at intervals of 3 hr. Refs. 637, 652.
32A	0.3 mile north of Old Faithful Inn, on northeast side of Firehole River:					
	Lion (Niobe) Geyser	201		do		Erupts to height of 50–60 ft several times a day. Refs. 576, 637.
	Lioness Geyser	203		do	562	Erupts rarely to maximum height of 80 ft; sometimes inactive for long periods. Refs. 637, 645.
	Big Cub Geyser	201		do		Erupts rarely to maximum height of 30 ft; sometimes inactive for long periods. Refs. 637, 645.
	Little Cub Geyser			do		Ref. 645.
	Giantess Geyser	202		do	562	Erupts rarely to height of 150–200 ft; sometimes inactive for long periods. Refs. 579, 626, 637, 647, 652, 665, 672, 679, 689.
	Midget Geyser			do		Erupts rarely to maximum height of 30 ft. Ref. 637.
	Beehive Geyser			do	562	Erupts to height of 200–220 ft two or more times a week. Refs. 579, 637, 645, 647, 649, 652, 661, 664, 672, 689.
32B	Solitary Geyser, 0.6 mile north of Old Faithful Inn	200		do	562	Erupts to maximum height of 25 ft at intervals of 2-6 min. Ref. 637.
33	Black Sand Basin, 0.8 mile west of Old Faithful Inn:					
	Cliff Geyser	190		do	562	Erupts to height of 40–50 ft once a day. Ref. 637.
	Whistle Geyser	149		do		Erupts infrequently to maximum height of 40 ft. Ref. 637.
	Rainbow Pool	151		do		Erupts to maximum height of 40 ft at irregular intervals; sometimes inactive for long periods. Ref. 637.
	Sunset Lake	169		do		Pool 45 yd in diameter.
	Emerald Pool	158		do		
33A	Castle Geyser, 0.4 mile northwest of Old Faithful Inn			do	562	Erupts to height of 65–100 ft at intervals of 12–16 hr. Large deposit of sinter. Refs. 587, 617, 637, 644, 647, 648, 652, 655, 661, 665, 689.
34	Old Faithful Geyser, near Old Faithful Inn			do	610	Erupts to height of 116–171 ft at intervals of 65 min. Large mound of gray sinter. Refs. 106, 563, 566, 576, 579, 590, 599, 617, 637, 648, 652, 659, 660, 677, 688, 689, 692.
34A	Pipeline Creek Springs, 0.5 mile southeast of Old Faithful Inn			do	562	
35	1 mile west of Summit Lake and 7 miles west-southwest of Old Faithful Inn			do		15 shallow, muddy springs. Deposit of sulfur. Ref. 561.
36	0.5 mile south-southeast of Summit Lake			do		
37	Lone Star Geyser, 2.7 miles south-southeast of Old Faithful Inn			do		Erupts to maximum height of 25 ft at intervals of 20–180 min. Cone of geyserite 12 ft high. Refs. 587, 637.
38	Shoshone Geyser Basin, 7.5 miles south-southeast of Old Faithful Inn:					
	Bead Geyser			do		Erupts to height of 10–20 ft. Abundant "geyser eggs." Ref. 637.
	Lion Geyser			do		Erupts to height of 10–12 ft. Ref. 637.
	Little Giant Geyser			do		Erupts to height of 10–50 ft twice a day. Ref. 637.
	Minute Man Geyser			do		Erupts to maximum height of 20 ft at intervals of 1–3 min. Ref. 637.
	Union Geyser			do		3 cones erupting simultaneously several times a week. Maximum height of eruption is 66 ft for northern cone, 114 ft for center cone, and 3 ft for southern cone. Ref. 637.
39	Bechter River Springs, 12.5 miles south-southwest of Old Faithful Inn			do		

Wyoming—Continued

No. on figure	Name or location	Temperature of water (°F)	Flow (gallons per minute)	Associated rocks	References on chemical quality	Remarks and additional references
40	Three River Junction Springs, near confluence of Phillips, Littles, and Ferris Forks of Bechter River.	----------	----------	Rhyolite (Tertiary)----------	----------------	
41	Tendoy Falls Springs, on Ferris Fork of the Bechter River.	----------	----------	----do----------	----------------	
42	Near northwest shore of Lewis Lake----------	Hot	----------	----------------	----------------	Large pools. Ref. 561.
42A	0.5 mile west of west shore of Lewis Lake----------	190–198	Small	----------------	----------------	Several springs. Ref. 561.
43	Near south outlet of Lewis Lake----------	154 (max)	Small	----------------	----------------	Do.
44	Deluge Geyser, near Witch Creek in Heart Lake Geyser Basin.	----------	----------	Rhyolite (Tertiary)----------	----------------	Erupts to height of 10–15 ft. Ref. 637.
44A	Spike Geyser, near Witch Creek in Heart Lake Geyser Basin.	----------	----------	----do----------	----------------	Erupts almost continuously. Ref. 637.
45	Rustic Geyser, 0.25 mile west of north end of Heart Lake.	201	----------	----do----------	----------------	Erupts to maximum height of 30 ft at intervals of 26–90 min. Ref. 637.
46	Near confluence of Snake and Lewis Rivers, 0.5 mile north-northeast of South Entrance to Yellowstone National Park.	158 (max)	----------	Limestone----------	----------------	
47	Snake Hot Springs, near the Snake River 5 miles upstream from confluence with Lewis River.	120–163	----------	Limestone near rhyolite----------	562----------	Several groups of springs. Terraces of travertine. Refs. 561, 621.
48	Near mouth of Basin Creek, 3 miles south of Heart Lake.	----------	----------	----------------	----------------	
49	Near Snake River, 0.5 mile downstream from mouth of Basin Creek.	----------	----------	Rhyolite overlying limestone.	----------------	
50	Washburn Hot Springs, 1.8 miles southeast of Dunraven Pass Ranger Station.	178–198	----------	Basaltic gravel or breccia----------	562	Several springs, including Inkpot Spring, and fumaroles in marshy area. Water from Inkpot Spring is black. Deposits of iron sulfide. Ref. 561.
51	Sulphur Creek Springs, 1.3 miles upstream from mouth of Sulphur Creek and 2 miles south-southeast of Dunraven Pass Ranger Station.	----------	----------	Rhyolite (Tertiary)----------	----------------	
52	Near mouth of Sulphur Creek, 3 miles south-southeast of Dunraven Pass Ranger Station.	----------	----------	----do----------	----------------	
53	0.5 mile northeast of Inspiration Point, on both sides of Yellowstone River.	----------	----------	----do----------	----------------	
54	Forest Springs, 1.2 miles east-southeast of Canyon Lodge at the Yellowstone River Falls.	----------	----------	----do----------	----------------	2 large mudpots and several small springs. Ref. 561.
55	0.5 mile south of Norris-Canyon Road and 4 miles west-southwest of Canyon Ranger Station.	----------	----------	----do----------	----------------	
56	Violet Springs, on tributary of Alum Creek 6 miles southwest of Canyon Ranger Station.	Hot	740	----do----------	561, 562----------	Deposit of sulfur.
57	Highland Hot Springs, on tributary of Alum Creek 3.5 miles southwest of Violet Springs (No. 56) and 1.1 miles north-northeast of Mary Lake.	----------	----------	----do----------	561, 562	
58	Alum Creek Springs, 2 miles east of Highland Hot Springs (No. 57).	194 (max)	Large	----do----------	----------------	Ref. 561.
59	1 mile southeast of Highland Hot Springs (No. 57) and 1 mile northeast of Mary Lake.	----------	----------	----do----------	----------------	2 springs, one rising in shallow basin and the other a small geyser. Ref. 561.
60	Elk Antler Creek Springs----------	----------	----------	----do----------	----------------	
61	Sulphur Spring (Crater Hills Geyser), 1 mile west of Yellowstone River and 4 miles south of Canyon Ranger Station.	194	Small	----do----------	562	Pool 20 ft in diameter; erupts to height of 5–6 ft at short intervals. Deposit of sulfur. Refs. 561, 576.
61A	Crater Hills Mudpots, on Lake-Canyon Road near mouth of Elk Antler Creek.	----------	----------	----do----------	----------------	5 small mud pools. Ref. 561.
61B	Dragon's Mouth Spring, on Lake-Canyon Road 6 miles (by road) northwest of Fishing Bridge.	160	----------	----do----------	562	Pulsating pool of clear water. Ref. 561.
61C	Mud Volcano, near Dragon's Mouth Spring (No. 61B).	185 (max)	----------	----do----------	562	Pool 30 ft in diameter. Ref. 561.
	Mud Geyser----------	----------	----------	----do----------	----------------	Erupts to maximum height of 12 ft every few sec. Ref. 561.
61D	Sulphur Caldron, on northeast side of Yellowstone River nearly opposite Dragon's Mouth Spring (No. 61B).	----------	----------	----do----------	----------------	Pool. Water contains much sulfur in suspension. Ref. 637.
62	Near west shore of West Thumb of Yellowstone Lake, 2 miles north of Thumb Ranger Station.	----------	----------	----do----------	----------------	
63	Near west shore of West Thumb of Yellowstone Lake, 1.5 miles north-northwest of Thumb Ranger Station.	200	----------	----do----------	----------------	
64	Near Thumb Ranger Station, on west shore of West Thumb of Yellowstone Lake:					
	Thumb Paintpots----------	200 (max)	----------	----do----------	562	Pools of pink and white mud. Also several small geysers. Refs. 561, 576, 637.
	King Geyser----------	----------	----------	----do----------	----------------	Spouts to maximum height of 6 ft at irregular intervals. Refs. 561, 637.
	Lakeshore Geyser----------	----------	----------	----do----------	----------------	Erupts to height of 15–25 ft at intervals of 35 min when lake level is low and at intervals of 2–4 days when submerged by lake water. Refs. 561, 637.
	Occasional Geyser----------	----------	----------	----do----------	----------------	Erupts to height of 25–60 ft at irregular intervals. Refs. 561, 637.
	Twin Geysers----------	----------	----------	----do----------	----------------	2 geysers erupting to height of 100–125 ft at intervals of 4–5 hr. Refs. 561, 637.
	Fishing Cone Spring, offshore from Thumb Paintpots.	----------	----------	----do----------	----------------	Refs. 561, 637.

No. on figure	Name or location	Temperature of water (°F)	Flow (gallons per minute)	Associated rocks	References on chemical quality	Remarks and additional references
				Wyoming—Continued		
65	Near Yellowstone River, 1 mile downstream from mouth of Lamar River.			Rhyolite (Tertiary)		
65A	Calcite Springs, in canyon of Yellowstone River 1 mile downstream from mouth of Tower Creek.	156-01		Breccia of andesitic and basaltic fragments.	562	Issue near veins of calcite and gypsum. Also fumaroles. Deposit of sulfur. Ref. 561.
66	Near Lamar River, 1 mile north-north-west of mouth of Cache Creek.			Rhyolite (Tertiary)		
67	Wahb Springs, in Death Gulch 2.2 miles upstream from mouth of Cache Creek.			___do___		Much CO_2. Ref. 637.
68	Near Deep Creek, 0.4 mile upstream from mouth of Shallow Creek.	Hot	100	___do___		Several springs. Ref. 561.
69	Near Deep Creek, 3 miles upstream from mouth of Shallow Creek.			___do___		Do.
70	Near Deep Creek, 4 miles upstream from mouth of Shallow Creek.			___do___		Do.
71	Near Deep Creek, 5 miles upstream from mouth of Shallow Creek.			___do___		Do.
72	Whistler Geyser, near west bank of Broad Creek 3 miles upstream from its mouth.	198		___do___	562	Erupts frequently. Ref. 637.
	Joseph's Coat Springs	Hot		___do___		Several springs. Scorodite deposited as coating on siliceous sinter. Refs. 609, 611, 620, 637, 702.
73	Near head of tributary to Broad Creek, 1.5 miles east of Whistler Geyser and Joseph's Coat Springs (No. 72).			___do___		
74	Near head of tributary to Broad Creek, 2 miles southeast of Whistler Geyser and Joseph's Coat Springs (No. 72).			___do___		
75	Hot Springs Basin, 1.5 miles north of Wapiti Lake.			___do___		Numerous fumaroles. Ref. 561.
76	Near tributary of Miller Creek, 2.7 miles northwest of Saddle Mountain.			___do___		
77	Near tributary of Lamar River, 2.6 miles west-southwest of Saddle Mountain.			___do___		
78	Near head of Moss Creek, 3 miles south-southwest of Whistler Geyser and Joseph's Coat Springs (No. 72).			___do___		
79	Bog Creek Springs, near head of Bog Creek, a tributary of Sour Creek.			___do___		
80	Head of unnamed tributary of Sour Creek, 1.5 miles northeast of Bog Creek Springs (No. 79).			___do___		
81	Along unnamed tributary of Sour Creek, 2 miles east of Bog Creek Springs (No. 79).			___do___		
82	Sour Creek Springs, 2.3 miles west of Fern Lake.			___do___		
83	Ponuntpa Springs, 0.6 mile southwest of Fern Lake.	113-180		___do___		Ref. 561.
84	Near east end of Fern Lake		Small	___do___		Do.
85	Near northwest end of White Lake	Warm	Small	___do___		Do.
86	Near southeast end of White Lake	Warm	Small	___do___		Do.
87	The Mudkettles, near Pelican Creek 1.5 miles east of southeast end of White Lake.			___do___		
88	The Mushpots, 1 mile southeast of the Mudkettles (No. 87).			___do___		
89	Near west end of Sulphur Hills, 1.8 miles south of Stonetop Mountain.	196		___do___		
90	Ebro Springs, 2.5 miles south-southwest of Stonetop Mountain.			___do___		
91	Vermilion Springs, near Pelican Creek, 2.3 miles south of Stonetop Mountain.			___do___		
92	Pelican Springs, at confluence of Pelican and Raven Creeks.			___do___		
93	Beach Springs, on shore of Mary Bay of Yellowstone Lake.			___do___		
94	Turbid Springs, near south end of Turbid Lake.	Hot	Small	___do___	562	Deposit of sulfur. Also boiling mud pots 0.5 mile west. Ref. 561.
95	Steamboat Springs, on northeast shore of Yellowstone Lake at Steamboat Point.	186-198		___do___	562	Also powerful steam vents. Ref. 576.
96	Butte Springs, on northeast shore of Yellowstone Lake, 1.5 miles southeast of Steamboat Point.	190 (max)	10	___do___	562	Several deep pools of clear water in area 300 yd long and 250 yd wide. Ref. 561.
97	DeMaris (Cody) Hot Springs, 4 miles southwest of Cody.	76-100		Deadwood Formation (Late Cambrian and Early Ordovician) or Tensleep Sandstone (Pennsylvanian and Permian).	137, 564, 598	Several springs. Deposit of sulfur. Resort and sanitarium. Refs. 144, 592, 594, 597, 703.
98	T. 55 N., R., 94 W., in Sheep Canyon of the Bighorn River near mouth of Five Springs Creek.	Warm		Folded Carboniferous or Triassic strata.		Several springs. Water used locally. Ref. 597.
99	T. 53 N., R. 94 W., near upper end of Black Canyon of the Bighorn River.	Warm	Small	Folded Carboniferous or Triassic strata.		Ref. 597.
100	Sec. 8, T. 48 N., R. 115 W., near the Snake River 2 miles south of boundary of Yellowstone National Park.	Hot	100	Lava (Tertiary) overlying shale (Cretaceous).		Refs. 144, 373, 564.
101	T. 39 N., R. 116 W., near the Snake River 4 miles downstream from mouth of Hobak River.	94	100	Chugwater Formation (Permian and Triassic) near fault.		Several springs. Water smells of sulfur. Used for bathing and irrigation.
102	Granite Hot Springs, in sec. 6, T. 39 N., R. 113 W.	110	360	Wasatch Formation (Eocene) near granite.		2 springs.
103	Near west bank of Salt River, 2.5 miles north of Auburn.	68-140	38	Limestone (Triassic or Jurassic).	676	Many springs. Water is salty. Deposit of tufa. Ref. 144.
104	Sec. 2, T. 38 N., R. 110 W., on the Green River near Wells.	Warm	Large	Limestone (Carboniferous)		6 springs.

No. on figure	Name or location	Temperature of water (°F)	Flow (gallons per minute)	Associated rocks	References on chemical quality	Remarks and additional references
				Wyoming—Continued		
105	T. 32 N., R. 107 W., near Fremont Butte.	Hot	Small	Granite_____	_____	Water used for bathing. Ref. 514.
106	Near Warm Spring Creek 4 miles northwest of Dubois.	84 (max)	_____	Tertiary strata overlying limestone (Carboniferous).	_____	Several springs. Deposit of tufa. Refs. 144, 442.
107	Near mouth of Little Warm Spring Creek, 3 miles southwest of Dubois.	68	_____	Carboniferous strata near granite.	_____	Do.
108	Fort Washakie Hot Springs, in sec. 2, T. 1S., R. 1 W., 24 miles west of Riverton.	110	2,000	Chugwater Formation (Permian and Triassic).	137, 564_____	Several springs rising in deep pools. Resort. Refs. 126, 144, 592, 594, 646.
109	T. 30 N., R. 97 W., 4 miles southwest of Hailey.	100–120	100	_____do_____	_____	Several springs. Water smells of H_2S. Used for irrigation. Refs. 144, 564, 594, 623.
110	T. 29 N., R. 96 W., near Sweetwater River 12 miles southwest of Myersville.	Warm	_____	Sandstone (Oligocene)_____	_____	Several springs. Water used locally. Ref. 623.
111	Big Horn (Thermopolis) Hot Springs, on the Bighorn River at Thermopolis.	135	>12,600	Tensleep Sandstone (Pennsylvanian and Permian).	137, 575, 585, 597, 598.	1 large spring and several small springs. Large deposit of tufa. Resort. Refs. 126, 144, 148, 564, 577, 586, 592, 638, 646, 704.
111A	3.5 miles northwest of Thermopolis, near sulfur deposits.	Hot	Small	Red beds (Triassic)_____	_____	Deposits of tufa and sulfur. Flow formerly much greater. Ref. 704.
112	Sec. 35, T. 32 N., R. 86 W., on Horse Creek near Independence.	Warm	Large	Oligocene strata near Chugwater Formation (Permian and Triassic).	_____	Several springs. Water used locally. Refs. 144, 623.
113	Alcova Hot Springs, in T. 30 N., R. 83 W., in Fremont Canyon of the North Platte River.	139	75	Faulted Upper Cretaceous strata.	564_____	Several springs. Resort. Refs. 144, 623.
114	T. 31 N., R. 71 W., near the North Platte River 9 miles south of Douglas.	Warm	_____	Folded Oligocene strata_____	_____	Water used for bathing and irrigation. Ref. 564.
115	Saratoga Hot Springs, in T. 17 N., R. 84 W.	120	10	Sandstone (Tertiary)_____	564_____	6 springs. Resort. Ref. 144.
116	10 miles northwest of Laramie_____	74	_____	Faulted Mesaverde Group (Late Cretaceous).	_____	Refs. 124, 144.

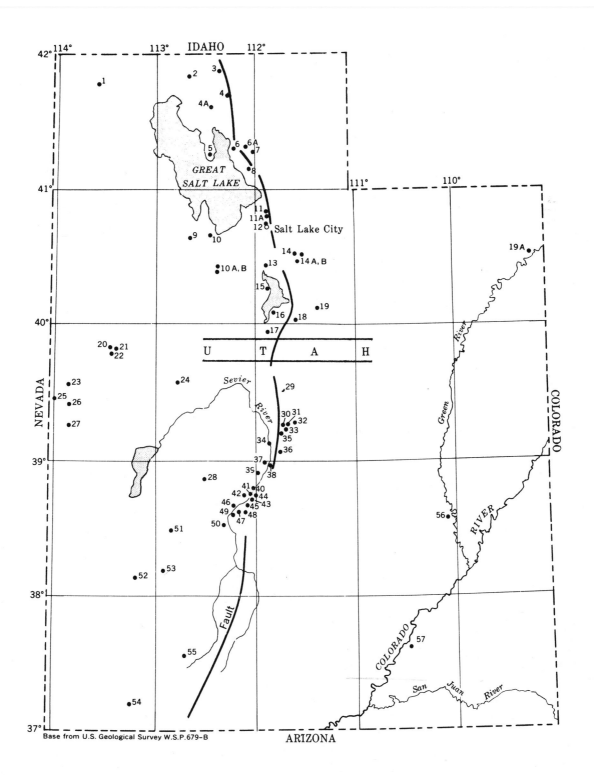

No. on figure	Name or location	Temperature of water (°F)	Flow (gallons per minute)	Associated rocks	References on chemical quality	Remarks and additional references
				Utah (See fig. 7.)		
1	Warm Springs in sec. 20, T. 12 N., R. 15 W., 17 miles north-northwest of Terrace railroad station.	Warm	900	Alluvium_____		Water used for irrigation. Ref. 508.
2	Blue (Honeyville) Springs, in T. 13 N., R. 5 W., 18 miles southeast of Snowville.	86	_____	___do.	508_____	6 springs. Refs. 144, 521.
3	Udy's Hot Springs, near the Malad River 2 miles southwest of Plymouth.	90–122	3,500	Carboniferous strata near Wasatch fault.		8 main springs. Water is saline. Used for bathing. Refs. 144, 508.
4	Crystal Springs, in T. 11 N., R. 2 W., 12 miles north of Brigham City.	121–134	_____	___do.	508	About 30 springs. Water used locally. Refs. 124, 133, 144, 505, 521.
4A	Near south end of Little Mountain, 7 miles west-northwest of Corinne.	Warm	Small	Paleozoic strata_____	508	
5	T. 6 N., R. 5 W., on east side of Promontory Point.	84		Faulted(?) schist and gneiss (Precambrian).		Ref. 144.
6	Utah (Bear River) Hot Springs, in T. 7 N., R 2 W., 8 miles northwest of Ogden.	131–144	110	Faulted quartzite (Cambrian).	20, 133, 137, 144, 409, 522.	12 springs. Water is saline and ferruginous. Ref. 138.
6A	Clay's Hot Springs, 10 miles north of Ogden.	140	50	Quartzite on Wasatch fault__		2 springs. Water is saline and ferruginous. Used for bathing. Ref. 512.
7	Patio Spring, 12 miles northeast of Ogden__	68	200	Lake beds (Quaternary)____		Water used for bathing.
8	Ogden Hot Springs, in T. 2 N., R. 1 W., at mouth of Ogden Canyon.	121; 150	Small	Syenite on Wasatch fault____	522	2 springs. Water used for bathing. Refs. 138, 144, 418, 505.
9	Big Springs, in T. 2 S., R. 8 W., on the west side of Stansbury Range.	74	_____	Carboniferous strata near fault.		2 springs. Water is brackish. Ref. 144.
10	Grantsville Warm Springs, 5 miles northwest of Grantsville.	74–91	50	Wasatch Formation (Eocene).		6 springs. Water is brackish; used for bathing. Deposit of calcareous tufa. Refs. 138, 144, 508.
10A	Morgan's Warm Springs, 4 miles southwest of Stockton.	80	500	_____do.		Water is ponded. Used for bathing and irrigation.
10B	Russell's Warm Springs, 4.5 miles southwest of Stockton.	90	200	_____do.		Water is ponded. Used for irrigation.
11	Beck's Hot Springs, 4 miles north of Salt Lake City.	128	_____	Paleozoic strata on Wasatch fault.	128, 133, 137, 418.	Several springs. Water smells of H₂S. Resort. Refs. 124, 144, 511, 512, 521, 686.
11A	Warm Springs, 2 miles north of Salt Lake City.	118	350	_____do.	525	Water used for bathing. Refs. 137, 511–513, 523.
12	Wasatch Springs, in the northwestern part of Salt Lake City.	130	350	Limestone (Carboniferous) near Wasatch fault.	525	Water used for bathing. Sanitarium. Refs. 133, 137, 144, 513, 523.
13	Crystal Springs, in T. 4 S., R. 1 W., 4 miles southwest of Draper.	70	_____	Alluvium_____		Several springs. Water used for bathing. Refs. 138, 144, 523.
14	Schneitter's Hot Pots, 4.5 miles northwest of Heber.	85–116	20	Wasatch Formation (Eocene) near Carboniferous limestone.	133, 137_____	20 main springs. Water used for bathing. Extensive deposit of tufa. Refs. 138, 144, 418, 514, 526.
14A	Luke's Hot Pots, 4 miles northwest of Heber.	78–110	30	_____do.		Several springs. Water used for bathing. Ref. 514.
14B	Buhler's Springs, 3.5 miles northwest of Heber.	80–108	10	_____do.		Several springs. Water used for bathing. Extensive deposit of tufa. Refs. 137, 510, 514.
15	Saratoga Springs, on northwest shore of Utah Lake.	111	211	Wasatch Formation (Eocene).		Several springs. Water used for bathing. Resort. Ref. 523.
16	T. 8 S., R. 1 E., on south shore of Utah Lake 8 miles northwest of Payson.	88	200	Alluvium_____		Water used locally. Ref. 523.
17	T. 10 S., R. 1 E., near the north end of Long Ridge 2 miles east of Goshen.	70	2,000	Faulted Carboniferous strata.		Several springs. Water used locally. Ref. 523.
18	Castilla Mineral Springs, in T. 9 S., R. 3 E., in Spanish Fork Canyon 15 miles south of Provo.	111; 145	_____	Carboniferous strata near Wasatch fault.		3 springs. Resort. Refs. 138, 144, 526.
19	Sec. 14, T. 8 S., R. 5 E., on Diamond Creek 15 miles east of Springville.	Warm	700	Wasatch Formation (Eocene).		2 springs. Water smells of sulfur.
19A	12 miles northeast of Jensen, in canyon of Green River.	90	10	Paleozoic or Mesozoic strata.		2 springs issuing at river edge.
20	Hot Springs, in T. 11 S., R. 14 W., at north end of Fish Springs Mountains and 3 miles north-northeast of Fish Springs (town).	74–78	_____	Alluvium near faulted Paleozoic strata.		Several springs. Water used locally. Refs. 138, 144, 506, 515, 520.
21	Big Spring, in T. 11 S., R. 14 W., 1 mile southeast of Hot Springs (No. 20).	85	_____	_____do.		3 springs. Refs. 144, 506, 520.
22	Fish Springs, in T. 11 S., R. 14 W., 4 miles southeast of Hot Springs (No. 20) and 3 miles east of Fish Springs (town).	80–140	_____	_____do.	406	7 springs. Water smells strongly of H₂S. Large deposit of tufa. Refs. 144, 406, 506, 515, 520.
23	Sec. 33, T. 14 S., R. 18 W., on Miller's Ranch 8 miles south of Trout Creek.	64	500	Alluvium_____		Several springs rising in pools. Water used for irrigation. Refs. 506, 520.
24	Abraham Springs in T. 14 S., R. 8 W., on Fumarole Butte, 19 miles north-north-west of Delta.	100–205	1,200	Fractured lava (Tertiary)___	507	20 springs. Deposit of manganese. Refs. 109, 144, 509, 512, 516, 520.
25	Sec. 31, T. 15 S., R. 19 W., in Snake Valley 1 mile west of Gandy.	82	Large	Limestone (lower Paleozoic)		Several springs. Water used for irrigation. Deposit of tufa. Ref. 520.
26	Sec. 9, T. 16 S., R. 18 W., in Snake Valley 2 miles south of Foote's Ranch.	68	1,000	Alluvium_____		Several springs rising in pools. Water used for irrigation. Refs. 144, 520.
27	Knoll Springs, in sec. 11, T. 18 S., R. 18 W., in Snake Valley 12 miles southeast of Smithville.	68–71	_____	Alluvium near Carboniferous strata.		Several springs. Water smells of H₂S. Used locally. Refs. 144, 520.
28	Sec. 24, T. 22 S., R. 6 W., 3 miles northwest of Hatton.	94	Large	Interbedded tuff and lava (Tertiary).		Water used for irrigation. Ref. 520.
29	Brewer's Springs, in secs. 13 and 24, T. 15 S., R. 2 E., 1 mile northwest of Wales.	57–62	400	Alluvium near faulted Wasatch Formation (Eocene).		3 springs. Water used for domestic purposes and irrigation. Ref. 524.
30	Lowry's Spring and Squires' Spring, in sec. 23, T. 18 S., R. 2 E., 3 miles south of Manti.	59; 62	40	Faulted Wasatch Formation (Eocene).		Water used for irrigation. Ref. 524.
31	Livingston Warm Springs, in sec. 13, T. 18 S., R. 2 E., 1 mile south of Manti.	62; 73	285	_____do.		2 main springs. Water used for domestic purposes and irrigation. Ref. 524.
32	Manti Springs, in sec. 17, T. 18 S., R. 3 E., 2 miles southeast of Manti.	59; 65	30	_____do.		Do.
33	Morrison Spring, in sec. 35, T. 18 S., R. 2 E., 2 miles northeast of Sterling.	61	2,500	_____		Water used for irrigation. Ref. 524.
34	Gunnison Spring, in sec. 18, T. 19 S., R. 1 E.	61	8	Alluvium_____		Water supply for cattle. Ref. 524.

No. on figure	Name or location	Temperature of water (°F)	Flow (gallons per minute)	Associated rocks	References on chemical quality	Remarks and additional references
				Utah—Continued		
35	Ninemile Warm Spring, in sec. 4, T. 19 S., R. 2 E.	72	900	Alluvium near faulted Wasatch Formation (Eocene).		Water used for domestic purposes and irrigation. Ref. 524.
36	Sec. 32, T. 20 S., R. 2 E., 8 miles northeast of Redmond.	58	15	Faulted Wasatch Formation.		Water used for irrigation. Ref. 524.
37	Redmond Springs, in secs. 11 and 12, T. 21 S., R. 1 W., near Redmond.	70	6,000	___do___		Several springs. Water used for domestic purposes and irrigation. Ref. 524.
38	Salt Spring, in sec. 17, T. 21 S., R. 1 E., 2 miles northeast of Salina.	72	2	Faulted Jurassic strata		Ref. 524.
39	Oak Spring and Christianson Spring, in sec. 1, T. 22 S., R. 2 W., 2 miles west of Aurora.	60	20	Faulted lava (Eocene)		Water supply for cattle. Ref. 524.
40	Herrin's Hole Spring, in sec. 23. T. 23 S., R. 2 W., 1 mile north of Glenwood.	63	450	___do___		Water used for irrigation. Ref. 524.
41	Cove Springs, in sec. 27, T. 23 S., R. 2 W., 1 miles west of Glenwood.	60	4,000	___do___		Several springs. Water used for irrigation. Ref. 524.
42	Richfield Hot Springs, in sec. 26, T. 23 S., R. 3 W.	74	1,500	Faulted limestone (Eocene)		Several springs. Water supply for town; also used for irrigation. Ref. 524.
43	Indian Spring and Parcel Creek Spring, in sec. 25, T. 23 S., R. 2 W., near Glenwood.	60	130	Faulted lava (Eocene)		Water used for domestic purposes and irrigation. Ref. 524.
44	Sec. 5, T. 24 S., R. 2 W., 2 miles southeast of Richfield.	52–61	4,500	Lava (Tertiary)		Several springs. Water used for irrigation. Ref. 524.
45	Sec. 25, T. 24 S. R. 3 W., 6 miles south of Richfield.	59	25	Alluvium overlying Wasatch Formation (Eocene).		Water used for domestic purposes and irrigation. Ref. 524.
46	Jericho Spring, in sec. 6, T. 25 S., R. 3 W., 2 miles northeast of Joseph.	65	700	Alluvium		Water used for irrigation. Ref. 524.
47	Johnson Spring, in sec. 27, T. 25 S., R. 3 W., 2 miles southeast of Joseph.	80	200	Faulted lava and tuff (Eocene).		Do.
48	Cooper Hot Springs, in sec. 15, T. 25 S., R. 3 W., 0.5 mile east of Monroe.	144–156	100	Faulted tuff (Tertiary)	524	Several springs. Water used for irrigation.
49	Joseph Hot Springs, in sec. 23, T. 25 S., R. 4 W., 1 mile southeast of Joseph.	135–146	30	Lava (Tertiary)		Several springs. Water used for irrigation. Deposit of tufa. Ref. 524.
50	Sevier Spring, in sec. 32, T. 25 S., R. 4 W.	59	100	Alluvium		Water used for domestic purposes; also water supply for cattle. Ref. 524.
51	Roosevelt (McKean's) Hot Spring, in T. 27 S., R. 9 W., on west slope of Mineral Mountains 15 miles northeast of Milford.	192	10	Granite	518	Water smells strongly of H_2S. Water supply for cattle. Deposits of tufa and sinter.
52	Warm Springs, secs. 21 and 28, T. 30 S., R. 12 W., 2 miles south-southwest of Thermo railroad siding.	90–175	20	Alluvium near faulted(?) lava (Tertiary).	518	About 16 springs issuing from a low ridge. Deposits of dense calcareous tufa. Water supply for cattle.
53	Radium (Dotson's) Warm Springs, in sec. 7, T. 30 S., R. 9 W., 1 mile east of Minersville.	97	57	Quartzite	518	3 springs. Water used for bathing and irrigation.
54	La Verkin Hot Springs, on Rio Virgin 2 miles north of Hurricane.	108–132	1,000	Faulted Triassic strata		Several springs. Refs. 133, 144.
55	T. 37 S., R. 7 W., 25 miles southwest of Panguitch.	Warm		Lava (Tertiary) overlying Wasatch Formation (Eocene).		Ref. 138.
56	Undine Springs, in T. 25 S., R. 17 E., in Labyrinth Canyon of the Green River.	Warm		Sandstone (Triassic)		Many small springs. Deposit of tufa. Ref. 138.
57	Warm Spring Canyon near its junction with "Narrow Canyon" or "Dark Canyon" of the Colorado River.	91		___do___		Ref. 138.

THE ETIQUETTE FOR BAPTISM.

No. on figure	Name or location	Temperature of water (°F)	Flow (gallons per minute)	Associated rocks	References on chemical quality	Remarks and additional references
				Montana		
1	Camas Hot Springs, in sec. 3, T. 21 N., R. 24 W.	110–114		Diorite sill in Belt Series (Precambrian).	137, 385	7 springs. Resort. Ref. 391.
2	Sec. 4, T. 21 N., R. 24 W., 1 mile west of Camas.	Warm		Belt Series (Precambrian)	385	Water used locally. Ref. 391.
3	Sec. 9, T. 18 N., R. 25 W., 4 miles south of Paradise.	114	20	_____do_____		7 springs. Water used for bathing.
4	Granite (Lolo) Hot Springs, 8 miles southwest of Woodson.	135	25	Granite	137	3 springs. Resort. Refs. 144, 383.
5	Warm Springs Creek, 6 miles north of Garrison.	Warm		Folded Cretaceous strata		Water used locally. Refs. 144, 148.
6	Sun River (Medicine) Hot Springs, on North Fork of Sun River 30 miles by road west of Augusta.	84	500	_____do_____		Resort. Refs. 144, 395.
7	Helena Hot Springs, 2 miles west of Helena.	122;141	30	Lower Paleozoic strata	128, 137 409	2 springs. Water used for bathing. Refs. 133, 393.
8	Big Warm Springs, in sec. 24, T. 26 N., R. 25 E., 6 miles south of Lodgepole.	72–86	10,000	Shale and limestone (Cretaceous).		7 springs. Water used locally.
9	Little Warm Springs, in sec. 32, T. 26 N., R. 26 E., 9 miles south of Lodgepole.	Warm	3,500	_____do_____		Water used locally.
10	Warm Spring, in sec. 19, T. 17 N., R. 18 E., on Warm Spring Creek 12 miles north of Lewistown.	68	80,000	Faulted Kootenai Formation (Early Cretaceous).		Water used for mining and milling, also for irrigation. Large deposit of tufa. Refs. 141, 379, 397.
11	Sec. 19, T. 12 N., R. 23 E., on Durphy Creek, 3 miles south of Tyler.	71	15,000	Folded Ellis Formation (Jurassic).		8 springs in area of several acres. Water used for irrigation.
12	Medicine Rock (Weeping Child) Hot Springs, on Weeping Child Creek, 15 miles southeast of Hamilton.	Hot	4,500	Granite		Several springs. Resort. Refs. 382, 383.
13	Sec. 31, T. 1 S., R. 22 W., 4 miles east of Slate Creek station.	Warm	330	_____do_____		5 springs.
14	Gallogly (Ross' Hole, Medicine) Hot Springs, in sec. 15, T. 1 S., R. 19 W., 4 miles south of Camp Creek station.	110–125	150	_____do_____		3 springs. Resort. Ref. 144.
15	Warm Springs, near Warm Springs railroad station, 10 miles northeast of Anaconda.	Warm		Tertiary strata overlying granite.	137	Resort. Ref. 144.
16	Anaconda Hot Springs, 3 miles east of Anaconda.	Warm		Travertine overlying limestone (Jurassic).		Several springs. Water used locally. Refs. 388, 395.
17	Gregson Hot Springs, 15 miles west of Butte.			Lava (Tertiary) overlying granite.		Several springs. Water used to heat greenhouse. Refs. 144, 395.
18	Alhambra Hot Springs, 17 miles south of Helena.	90–134		Granite	137	22 springs. Resort. Refs. 133, 393.
19	Boulder Hot Springs, 3 miles southeast of Boulder.	125–187	Large	Fissured granite	133, 137, 393	Many springs. Resort. Refs. 109, 395.
20	Pipestone Springs, 20 miles southeast of Butte.	Hot		Granite	137	Several springs. Resort. Refs. 393, 395.
21	Bedford Springs, on north side of Indian Creek 3.5 miles northwest of Townsend.	74	1,400	Gravel overlying Tertiary strata.	384, 387	3 main and several other springs. Water used for irrigation.
22	Kimpton (Warner) Warm Springs, on branch of Crow Creek, 7 miles west of Toston.	65	100	Lake beds (Miocene)	384, 387	2 springs. Water used locally. Ref. 144.
22A	Big Spring, on east bank of Missouri River 4 miles southeast of Toston.	59	29,000	Madison Limestone (Mississippian).	384, 387	Water used for irrigation.
23	Plunket's (Mockel, Nave's Warm) Spring, at head of Warm Creek, 10 miles southwest of Toston.	62	4,000	_____do_____	384, 387	Several springs. Water used for irrigation.
24	White Sulphur (Brewer's) Springs	95–125	500	Lake beds (Miocene) overlying Belt Series (Precambrian).	128, 133, 380, 392, 396.	9 springs. Resort.
25	Big Hole Hot Springs, at Jackson	132 (max)	1,500	Tertiary strata overlying Belt Series (Precambrian).		About 100 springs. Resort. Refs. 144, 386.
26	Elkhorn Hot Springs, in sec. 29, T. 4 S., R. 12 W., on Miller Creek 6 miles north of Polaris.	120–150	110	Granite		7 springs. Resort.
27	Ziegler Hot Springs, near Apex	Hot		Folded Cretaceous strata		Several springs. Water used locally. Ref. 391.
28	Lovell Springs, in sec. 21, T. 8 S., R. 9 W., 9 miles southwest of Dillon.	72	1,125	Lava (Tertiary)		4 springs. Water used locally.
29	Brown (Ryan Canyon) Springs, in sec. 30, T. 8 S., R. 9 W., 11 miles southwest of Dillon.	72	360	Lava (Tertiary) overlying limestone (Carboniferous).		6 springs. Water used locally.
30	Barkel's Hot Springs, at Silverstar	Hot	50	Lake beds (Tertiary) overlying granite.		4 springs. Water used for bathing.
31	Clark's Warm (Potosi Hot) Springs, on south branch of Willow Creek, 5 miles south of Pony.	100–120	550	Granite		About 10 springs. Refs. 133, 389.
32	Hapgood (Norris) Hot Springs, on Hot Spring Creek near Norris.	80–122	50	Syenite		5 springs. Water used for bathing. Refs. 138, 388, 389.
33	Puller's Hot Springs, on upper Ruby Creek, 10 miles northwest of Virginia City.	95; 108	150	Schist and gneiss (Precambrian).		2 springs. Resort. Refs. 133, 144.
34	Sec. 18, T. 12 S., R. 1 E., 3 miles southwest of Cliff Lake.	Warm	100	Lava (Quaternary)		
35	Bozeman (Ferris, Matthews) Hot Springs, on West Gallatin River, 7 miles west of Bozeman.	137	250	Tertiary strata	128, 133, 137, 144, 380.	Resort. Ref. 389.
36	Hunter's Hot Springs, 20 miles northeast of Livingston.	148–168	1,500	Faulted Livingston Formation (Upper Cretaceous and Paleocene).	128?, 133, 137, 409?	3 groups, totaling about 25 individual springs. Deposit of gypsum. Resort. Refs. 109, 389, 394, 395.
37	Emigrant Gulch Warm Springs (Chico Spring), on Emigrant Creek near Chico.	102	240	Lava (Quaternary) overlying Precambrian rocks.	128, 144, 409	Water used for bathing.
38	Corwin Hot Springs, in sec. 25, T. 8 S., R. 7 E.	[1] 120 (max)		Lava overlying schist (Precambrian).		Several springs. Resort. Ref. 391.
39	Bear Creek Springs, in sec. 19, T. 9 S., R. 9 E., 3 miles south of Gardiner.	90	30	Lava (Quaternary) overlying Precambrian rocks.		2 springs. Water used locally.
40	Anderson's Spring, in sec. 29, T. 3 S., R. 13 E., near Boulder Creek 3 miles southwest of Hubble.	70	90	Limestone (Cretaceous)		Water used for bathing. Ref. 390.

No. on figure	Name or location	Temperature of water (°F)	Flow (gallons per minute)	Associated rocks	References on chemical quality	Remarks and additional references
			Arizona			
1	Pakoon (Pahgun) Spring, on tributary of Grand Wash, 18 miles north of Colorado River.	100	---------	Lava (late Tertiary) --------	-----------------	Ref. 138.
2	Sec. 23, T. 30 N., R. 23 E., 5 miles south of Hoover (Boulder) Dam.	Hot	---------	Lava (Tertiary) ----------		
3	Lava Warm Springs, near Lava Falls Rapids in the Grand Canyon of the Colorado River.	89	6,700	Granite ---------		Several springs. Refs. 138, 144.
4	Sec. 33, T. 18 N., R. 19 W., 25 miles southwest of Kingman.	Warm	---------	Lava (Tertiary) ----------		
5	Sec. 32, T. 15 N., R. 6 E., 10 miles northeast of Camp Verde.	72	50	Lava (Tertiary) overlying sandstone (Permian).		3 springs. Water used locally.
6	Verde Hot Springs, 0.5 mile northwest of Childs.	104	75	Lava (Tertiary) ----------		Several springs. Resort.
7	6 miles south of St. Johns	74	2	Sandstone (Triassic) -------		Deposit of tufa.
8	Castle (Monroe) Hot Springs, in sec. 3, T. 7 N., R. 1 W., on Castle Creek, 50 miles south of Prescott.	115–122	280	Lava (Tertiary) ----------	133, 137	2 springs. Water used for bathing. Refs. 144, 187, 194.
9	Salt Banks, in sec. 33, T. 6 N., R. 17 E., 30 miles west of Whiteriver.	Warm	---------	Sandstone (Cambrian) ------		Large group of springs. Water used locally.
10	Soda Warm Spring, in sec. 13, T. 6 N., R. 19 E., 23 miles west of Whiteriver.	65		Limestone of Supai Formation (Pennsylvanian and Permian).	-----------------	
11	Agua Caliente Springs, in sec. 19, T. 5 S., R. 10 W., 15 miles northeast of Palomas.	99–104	---------	Lava (Quaternary) ----------	137, 192	Several springs. Resort.
12	Sec. 35, T. 5 S., R. 19 E., 3 miles north of Aravaipa.	90	6	Lava (Tertiary) ----------		Water used for bathing.
13	Near Gila River, 3 miles north of Fort Thomas.	----------	---------	Lake beds (Pliocene) --------		Do.
14	Indian Hot Springs, 8 miles northwest of Pima.	81–118	300	-----do ----------------	189, 190	5 springs and 1 well 600 ft deep. Resort.
15	Near Bonito Creek, in T. 4 S., R. 27 E., 25 miles east of Fort Thomas.	Warm	---------	Lava (Tertiary) -----------		
16	T. 4 S., R. 28 E., 10 miles west of Morenci.	Hot	Small	-----do ----------------		Ref. 191.
17	Clifton Hot Springs	127–160		-----do ----------------	137, 191	4 springs. Resort. Refs. 188, 328.
18	Aguajito (Quitabaquito), near Mexican border.	Warm		Alluvium near schist -------	-----------------	Water used for village supply and irrigation. Ref. 186.
19	Hooker's Hot Springs, in sec. 6, T. 13 S., R. 21 E., 10 miles northeast of Cascabel.	130	40	Faulted granite ----------	-----------------	2 main springs. Water used for bathing.
20	Agua Caliente Spring, in sec. 13, T. 20 S., R. 13 E., 5 miles east of Amado.	90	50	Gravel (Quaternary) overlying red shale and sandstone (Cretaceous?).	-----------------	Water used for bathing. Refs. 138, 184, 193.
21	Sec. 7, T. 18, S., R. 31 E., 6 miles southwest of Paradise.	----------	---------	Quartzite dike near lava (Tertiary).	-----------------	Water used locally.
			Washington			
1	Baker Hot Spring, in sec. 30, T. 38 N., R. 9 E., on east side of Mount Baker.	108	7	Lava (upper Tertiary) overlying granite.	-----------------	
2	Sol Duc Hot Springs, in sec. 32, T. 29 N., R. 9 W., 14 miles (by road) southwest of Crescent Lake.	100–132	50	Metamorphic rocks (pre-Tertiary).		3 main and 8 smaller springs in 1-acre area. Resort.
3	Olympic Hot Springs, in sec. 27, T. 29 N., R. 8 W., 11.5 miles (by trail) southwest of Elwha post office.	120–125	135	-----do ----------------		17 springs in 5-acre area. Resort.
4	Sulphur Creek Spring, in sec. 30, T. 32 N., R. 12 E., 1 mile north of Sulphur Creek Shelter.	98	4	Granite ----------------	-----------------	
5	White Chuck Hot Springs, in sec. 1, T. 30 N., R. 12 E., near the White Chuck River.	100–110	30	-----do ----------------		4 springs. Water used for bathing. Deposit of iron-stained tufa.
6	San Juan Hot Springs, in sec. 25, T. 28 N., R. 11 E., on the North Fork of Skykomish River 5 miles east of Galena.	100	25	-----do ----------------		3 springs. Ref. 548.
7	Scenic (Great Northern) Hot Springs, in sec. 28, T. 26 N., R. 13 E., 5 miles west of Scenic.	122	30	-----do ----------------	546, 548	Several springs. Water is sulfurous; is piped 2 miles to hotel. Resort.
8	McDaniels Hot Springs, in sec. 15, T. 23 N., R. 11 E.	114–127	30	-----do ----------------		4 springs. Resort.
9	Hot Springs, in sec. 21, T. 20 N., R. 9 E., at Hot Springs railroad station.	120–122	---------	Basalt (Tertiary) ----------	548	5 springs. Resort.
10	Clerf Spring, in sec. 5, T. 17 N., R. 20 E., 8 miles east of Ellensburg.	68	1,100	Basalt (Tertiary) overlying sandstone (Miocene).		Water used for irrigation. Refs. 544, 549, 550.
11	Ohanapecosh Hot Springs, in sec. 4, T. 14 N., R. 10 E., near south base of Mount Rainier.	109–120	60	Basalt (Tertiary) ----------		5 springs. Resort and sanitarium. Ref. 660.
12	Sec. 9, T. 11 N., R. 15 E., on the North Fork of Simcoe Creek.	90	40	-----do ----------------		Several springs. Water used for bathing. Ref. 546.
12A	North slope of Mount St. Helens	142–190		Lava (Quaternary) ----------		Small fumaroles. Ref. 547.
12B	Crater of Mount Adams	Hot	---------	-----do ----------------		Steam vents and small fumaroles. Ref. 547.
13	Nicolai Spring, in sec. 15, T. 11 N., R. 23 E., 10 miles north of Sunnyside.	66	300	Ellensburg Formation (Miocene).	-----------------	Water used for irrigation. Ref. 551.
14	Sec. 16, T. 6 N., R. 13. E., 5 miles southeast of Glenwood.	76	Large	Basalt (Tertiary) ----------		Several springs. Gas rises with water. Water used for irrigation. Ref. 546.
15	Blockhouse Mineral Springs, in sec 12, T. 4 N., R. 14 E., 8 miles west of Goldendale.	67	50	-----do ----------------	137, 546	2 springs. Resort.
16	Cascade Warm (Moffet's Hot) Springs, in sec. 16, T. 2 N., R. 7 E., near Cascade.	96	20	-----do ----------------	137	4 springs. Resort. Refs. 133, 546.

No. on figure	Name or location	Temperature of water (°F)	Flow (gallons per minute)	Associated rocks	References on chemical quality	Remarks and additional references

Colorado

No. on figure	Name or location	Temperature of water (°F)	Flow (gallons per minute)	Associated rocks	References on chemical quality	Remarks and additional references
1	Juniper Hot Springs, in sec. 16, T. 6 N., R. 94 W.	102–105	25	Cretaceous strata	322	Several springs. Resort. Ref. 323.
2	Routt Hot Springs, 7 miles north of Steamboat Springs (No. 2A).	148–150	130	Fractured gneiss near contact with granite.		3 springs. Water used for bathing.
2A	Steamboat Springs	103–150	2,000	Faulted sandstone (Dakota?).	137, 322	150 springs. Deposit of tufa. Resort. Refs. 313, 325–327.
3	Hot Sulphur Springs	90–118	40	Cretaceous strata near granite.	137, 322	25 springs. Strong odor of sulfur. Deposit of tufa. Resort and sanitarium. Refs. 317, 325–327, 513.
4	Moffat (Eldorado) Spring, 12 miles southwest of Boulder.	70	10	Faulted marl (Jurassic)	322	Refs. 325, 327.
5	Hot Soda Springs at Idaho Springs	98–108	50	Fractured syenite near gneiss.	137, 322, 335	Several springs. Resort. Refs. 140, 317, 325, 327, 333, 334.
6	Glenwood Springs	106–150	3,000	Faulted Cretaceous strata	137, 322	Many springs issuing from bank and bed of Colorado River. Resort. Refs. 325, 326, 334.
7	Big Dotsero Spring, on north bank of Colorado River 1.5 miles downstream from Dotsero.	84	400	Limestone (Carboniferous)	322	Water used for bathing.
8	Avalanche Springs, near Avalanche	112–134	200	Diorite intrusion in Carboniferous strata.	322	5 springs issuing along Rock Creek (Crystal River). Water used for bathing. Ref. 324.
9	Conundrum Spring, 16 miles south of Aspen.	100	25	Decomposed granite	322	
10	Alkali Springs, near north end of bridge over the Gunnison River at Austin.	72	5	Sandstone (Dakota?)	322	Several small springs.
11	Sec. 21, T. 13 S., R. 89 W., 10 miles east of Somerset.	90	3	Sandstone (Cretaceous)		4 springs.
12	Ranger (Cement Creek) Spring, 1.5 miles above mouth of Cement Creek.	83	350	Limestone near granite	322	Deposit of tufa.
13	Sec. 18, T. 14 S., R. 84 W., 2.5 miles above mouth of Cement Creek.	100	1,800	Limestone (Cretaceous)		
14	Waunita (Tomichi) Hot Springs, on Hot Springs Creek, 28 miles east of Gunnison.	140–160	1,000	Sandstone (Paleozoic?)	137	2 groups of springs totaling more than 100 individual springs. Resort. Refs. 144, 322.
15	Cebolla (Powderhorn) Hot Springs (Ojo de los Caballos), 6 miles south of Powderhorn.	79–114	100	Granite and gneiss		2 groups of springs totaling about 20 individual springs. Resort. Refs. 322, 330.
16	Rhodes Spring, 8 miles southwest of Fairplay.	79	300	Alluvium	322	Water used locally.
17	Hartsell Hot Springs, 25 miles east of Leadville.	105–134	10	Mesozoic strata near granite.	137, 322	5 springs. Resort. Refs. 138, 317.
18	Mound Soda (Currant Creek) Spring, 20 miles northwest of Parkdale.	68		Granite		Refs. 138, 335.
19	Cottonwood (Buena Vista Hot) Springs, 6 miles west of Buena Vista.	120–144	150	Granite near monzonite intrusion.	322	5 springs. Campground.
20	Mount Princeton (Heywood Hot, Chalk Creek Hot) Springs, 3 miles west of Nathrop.	98–150	50	do		4 main and about 30 other springs. Resort. Refs. 322, 325, 335.
21	Poncha Springs	80–168	500	Granite	137	About 100 springs. Water contains 12 ppm of fluorine. Resort. Deposit of tufa. Refs. 109, 315, 317, 322, 325, 326, 331.
22	Wellsville Warm Spring, 5 miles northwest of Howard.	94	150	Carboniferous strata	322	Water used locally. Ref. 138.
22A	Canon City:					
	Near east end of Royal Gorge of Arkansas River.	101				Pumped well 10 ft deep. Ref. 317
	Fremont Natatorium	100	140	Sandstone (Dakota?)		Flowing well 1,665 ft deep.
23	Chamberlain (Mineral) Hot Springs, in sec. 12, T. 45 N., R. 9 E., 6 miles south of Villa Grove.	116–133	50	Lava overlying sedimentary strata.		30 springs. Deposit of tufa. Resort. Refs. 322, 332.
24	Valley View (Orient) Hot Springs, in sec. 31, T. 46 N., R. 10 E., 7 miles southeast of Villa Grove.	72–99	200	Quartzite near granite	332	5 springs. Water used for bathing. Ref. 322.
25	Red Creek (Siloam, Parnassus) Springs, 12 miles southwest of Pueblo.	59–73	5	Contact of Upper Cretaceous strata and gneiss.	322, 328	5 springs. Water used locally. Deposit of tufa.
26	Geyser Warm Spring, at Placerville	94	5	Mesozoic strata	322	Water used for bathing.
27	Orvis (Ridgway, Uncompahgre) Hot Spring, 2 miles southeast of Ridgway.	132	300	Alluvium overlying faulted Pennsylvanian strata.		Water used for bathing and irrigation. Refs. 316, 317, 322, 330.
28	Ouray Hot Springs	100–158	200	Faulted Hermosa Formation (Pennsylvanian).	137, 316	3 groups of springs. Water supply for 2 sanitariums and municipal swimming pool. Resort. Refs. 312, 317, 322, 332.
29	Sec. 33, T. 41 N., R. 11 W., 200 yd southeast of Dunton Store.	110	20	Limestone (Cretaceous)		Water used locally.
30	Iron Spring, 0.75 mile north of Rico	82	30	Sandstone and shale (Permian).	322	Deposit of limonite.
31	Wagon Wheel Gap Springs	132–150	100	Granite cut by dikes	137, 318, 319, 328	3 springs. Large deposit of tufa. Resort. Refs. 109, 128, 315, 317, 322, 325.
32	Sec. 26, T. 38 N., R. 1 W., 26 miles northeast of Pagosa Springs.	100; 120	50	Granite		2 springs.
33	Shaw's Spring, 6 miles north of Del Norte	88	10	Sandstone (Tertiary) near igneous rock.	322	Water used locally.

No. on figure	Name or location	Tempera-ture of water (°F)	Flow (gallons per minute)	Associated rocks	References on chemical quality	Remarks and additional references
				New Mexico		
1	Sec. 32, T. 11 N., R. 2 W., 10 miles south of Shiprock.	68	3	Mancos Shale (Upper Cretaceous) intruded by porphyry dike.	144, 328, 460	Water smells of H_2S. Water supply or cattle.
2	Sec. 8, T. 7 N., R. 2 W., 5 miles north of Newcomb.	65	3	do		Do.
3	Sec. 16, T. 7 N., R. 2 W., 4 miles north of Newcomb.	67	7	do		Do.
4	Sec. 23, T. 25 N., R. 8 E., 0.75 mile northwest of La Madera.	80	10	Lake beds (Tertiary)		Several springs.
5	Sec. 24, T. 25 N., R. 8 E., 1 mile northeast of La Madera.	100	5	Granite		
6	Sec. 25, T. 25 N., R. 8 E., 0.25 mile north of La Madera.	90	15	Lake beds (Tertiary)		
7	Sec. 35, T. 25 N., R. 8 E., 1 mile southwest of La Madera.	100	5	Granite		
8	Ojo Caliente Springs, 12 miles northwest of Barranca.	98–113	350	Gneiss intruded by dikes	133, 137, 328, 458, 460, 463, 464.	5 springs. Tufa deposit contains fluorite. Resort.
9	Togay Springs, in sec. 33, T. 19 N., R. 15 W., 20 miles east of Tohatchie.	65	65	Mesaverde Group (Late Cretaceous).		Many small pools. Water supply for cattle.
10	Murray Spring, in sec. 29, T. 20 N., R. 3 E., 15 miles north of Jemez Springs (town).	130	150	Basalt (upper Tertiary)		
11	San Antonio Springs, in sec. 7, T. 20 N., R. 4 E., on San Antonio Creek 20 miles north of Jemez Springs (town).	120	50	do		Refs. 461, 465.
12	Sulphur Springs, in sec. 3, T. 19 N., R. 3 E., 12 miles north of Jemez Springs (town).	76–167	500	Andesite and rhyolite (Tertiary).	461, 466	8 springs. Water smells of H_2S. Refs. 460, 465.
13	Soda Dam Springs, in sec. 15, T. 18 N., R. 2 E., in Canyon de San Diego, 2 miles north of Jemez Hot Springs (No. 15).	75–105	10	Limestone (Carboniferous) faulted against granite.	461, 465	Several springs. Large deposit of tufa. Refs. 457, 460, 466.
14	McCauley Spring, in sec. 4, T. 18 N., R. 3 E., 7 miles north of Jemez Springs (town).	100	110	Lava (upper Tertiary)		
15	Jemez Hot Springs (Ojos Calientes), in sec. 22, T. 18 N., R. 2 E., 12 miles north of Jemez (pueblo).	94–168	200	Faulted Chinle Formation (Triassic).	137, 144, 460, 461, 465, 466.	1 group of 10 and another group of 40 springs. Resort. Refs. 133, 328, 457, 464.
16	Phillips Springs, in T. 16 N., R. 1 W., 10 miles west of Jemez (pueblo) and 1 mile northeast of Rio Salado.	70	Small	Fault contact between Chinle Formation (Triassic) and Carboniferous strata.	466	About 40 springs in 30-acre area. Deposits of travertine. Refs. 457, 461, 465.
17	Indian (Jemez) Springs, in T. 16 N., R. 2 E., 2 miles north of San Ysidro.	120		Faulted Chinle Formation (Triassic).		Several springs. Water used locally. Refs. 457, 461, 465, 466.
18	San Ysidro Hot Springs, in sec. 8, T. 15 N., R. 1 E., 7 miles southwest of San Ysidro.	86 (max)		do	460, 466	40 springs. Water is strongly carbonated. Used locally. Refs. 457, 461.
19	San Ysidro Warm Springs, in secs. 3, 9, 10, T. 15 N., R. 1 E.	68	Small	do	137, 466	Several springs.
20	Las Vegas Hot Springs, 6 miles northwest of Las Vegas.	80–140	100	Contact of Carboniferous strata with Precambrian rocks.	133, 137, 144, 335, 345.	6 springs. Water smells of H_2S. Used for bathing. Refs. 328, 459, 464.
21	Ojo Caliente Springs, in sec. 21, T. 8 N., R. 20 W., 12 miles southwest of Zuni.	80	500	Sandstone and shale (Triassic).	328	2 springs. Water used for bathing and irrigation. Refs. 144, 460.
22	Quelites Mineral Spring, in T. 8 N., R. 2 W., on north side of San Jose River 2 miles northwest of Quelites.	80	3	Sandstone (Cretaceous)	137	Water used locally. Deposit of tufa. Ref. 460.
23	Socorro Warm Springs, 1.5 miles southwest of Socorro.	93	500	Lake beds (Tertiary) near lava.		Several springs. Water supply for Socorro. Refs. 460, 464, 467.
24	Ojo Caliente, in sec. 31, T. 8 S., R. 7 W., 15 miles northwest of Monticello.	85	1,200	Rhyolite (Tertiary)		7 springs. Refs. 144, 460.
25	Sec. 23, T. 12 S., R. 20 W., 1 mile south of Pleasanton.	80–124	50	Lava (upper Tertiary)		8 springs. Water used locally.
26	Sec. 30, T. 11 S., R. 12 W., 1 mile south of DD Bar Ranch.	80	50	Lava agglomerate (Quaternary).		
27	Sec. 19, T. 12 S., R. 13 W., on Diamond Creek near its mouth.	151	30	Lava (Tertiary)		Refs. 138, 144, 460.
28	Sec. 26, T. 13 S., R. 16 W., near Turkey Creek.	80	20	do		
29	Sec. 3, T. 14 S., R. 16 W., on Turkey Creek 3 miles above its confluence with the Gila River.	Hot	20	Lava (Tertiary)		
30	Gila Hot Springs, in sec. 5, T. 13 S., R. 13 W., on the Gila River near Diamond Creek.	90–100	900	do		4 springs. Water used for bathing. Refs. 138, 144, 460.
31	Sec. 3, T. 13 S., R. 13 W., on the Gila River.	Hot	30	do		Water used locally.
32	Sec. 20, T. 13 W., R. 13 W., on the Gila River.	Hot	30	do		
33	Sec. 16, T. 14 S., R. 14 W., on the Gila River.	Hot	20	do		
34	Hudson's Hot Springs, 4 miles northwest of Mimbres.	142		do	133	Several springs. Water used for bathing. Refs. 135, 144.
35	Apache Tejo Warm Springs, 7 miles north of Whitewater.	97	2,000	Alluvium near lava		Several springs. Water used locally. Refs. 138, 144.
36	Faywood Hot Springs, in T. 20 S., R. 11 W., 6 miles northeast of Faywood.	142	120	Lava (Tertiary)	345	Several springs issuing from mound of tufa. Resort. Ref. 526.
37	Hot Springs (Palomas), near Truth or Consequences.	90–105	10	Limestone (Pennsylvanian) faulted against granite.	137	Several springs and wells. Water used for bathing. Resort and State Hospital for crippled children. Refs. 460, 468.
38	Radium Hot Springs, near Radium Springs railway station 17 miles north of Las Cruces.	165; 185	Small	Rhyolite (Tertiary)		2 springs. Water is brackish. Used for bathing and heating hotel. Refs. 133, 137.

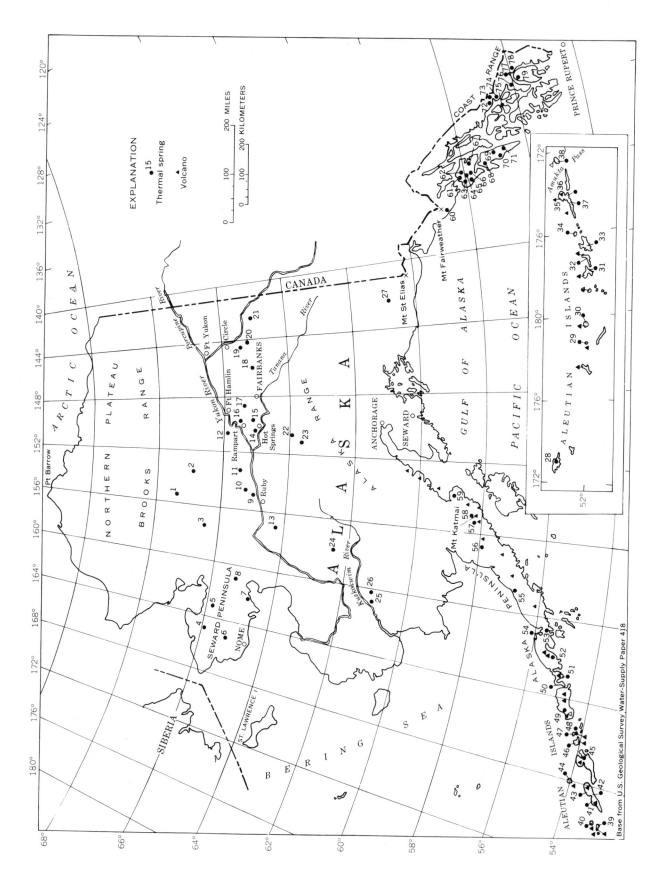

EXPLANATION

• 15
Thermal spring

▲
Volcano

Base from U.S. Geological Survey Water-Supply Paper 418

[Data chiefly from refs. 172 and 178.   Principal chemical constituents are expressed in parts per million]

No. on fig. 9	Name or location	Temperature of water (°F)	Flow (gpm)	Total dissolved solids (ppm)	Principal chemical constituents	Associated rocks	Remarks and additional references
1	Near head of Reed River	100				Probably schist	Pool 20 ft in diameter. Small deposit of tufa. Ref. 176.
2	On upper course of Alatna River.	Warm	Large			Paleozoic schist and limestone.	Numerous springs near river channel.
3	Near head of Selawik River	Warm				Probably Mesozoic or older strata.	
4	Arctic, on Hot Springs Creek	150	10			Probably granite intrusive in gneiss.	Several springs issuing along creek for distance of 0.5 mile. Small amount of H$_2$S. Large mounds of tufa. Bath cabin. Refs. 154, 165.
5	Near Inmachuk River	100	Large			Crystalline limestone	Ref. 170.
6	Kruzgamepa, 70 miles north of Nome.	100; 156	8	[1] 5,955	SiO$_2$ (87); Ca (545); Na (1,587); K (61); SO$_4$ (25); Cl (3,450); small amount of free H$_2$S.	Alluvium overlying granite.	2 main springs; also much seepage. Small deposit of salt. Water used for bathing and irrigation. Ref. 165.
7	Near Kwiniuk River	Hot				Probably Paleozoic strata	2 small groups of springs. Free H$_2$S.
8	On tributary of Sweepstake Creek.	Hot				do	
9	Horner, 0.75 mile north of Yukon River.	86–120	45	[2] 292	SiO$_2$ (29); Na+K (58); HCO$_3$ (22); CO$_3$ (32); SO$_4$ (45); Cl (39); small amount of free H$_2$S.	Fractured granite	1 main and 7 smaller springs. Temperature of water from main spring, 117°F. Water used for domestic supply and irrigation.
10	Melozitna, 16 miles north of Kokrines.	131	130	442	SiO$_2$ (78); Na+K (107); SO$_4$ (61); Cl (92); small amount of free H$_2$S.	Granite, probably intruded into Paleozoic strata.	Issues on creek bank. Small deposits of tufa and sulfur. Bath cabin.
11	Little Melozitna, 27 miles north of Hub roadhouse.	82–99.5	60	[1] 350	SiO$_2$ (80); Na; HCO$_3$; Cl; free CO$_2$, H$_2$S.	Granite intrusive in schist.	Main and 4 smaller springs. Water from main spring is hottest. Bathing pool.
12	On Ray River, 35 miles above its mouth.	130				Granite intrusive	Free H$_2$S. Water used for bathing and irrigation.
13	On tributary of Innoko River.	Hot	Moderately large			Probably Mesozoic strata	
14	Baker, near north bank of Tanana River.	101–136	145	417	SiO$_2$ (59); Na (121); HCO$_3$ (86); SO$_4$ (48); Cl (120).	Granite intrusive	3 springs. Analysis is for water having temperature of 125°F. Water used for bathing and irrigation.
15	Hutlinana, 8.5 miles east of Eureka post office.	114	50	634	SiO$_2$ (44); Na+K (208); HCO$_3$ (494); SO$_4$ (67); Cl (38); free CO$_2$.	Lower Cretaceous quartzite.	Bathing pool; cabins.
16	Near Little Minook Creek	Hot	Small			Granite, probably intruded into Paleozoic strata.	
17	Near Tolovana River	130	Small			Granite intrusive in schist.	Water tastes alkaline. Free CO$_2$, H$_2$S.
18	Chena, 62 miles east-north-east of Fairbanks.	72–153	220	338	SiO$_2$ (77); Na+K (94); HCO$_3$ (118); SO$_4$ (78); free H$_2$S.	do	10 main springs. Analysis is for water having temperature of 149°F. Water used for bathing and irrigation.
19	42 miles southwest of Circle	100–134	130	[1] 813	SiO$_2$ (82); Na (248); HCO$_3$ (173); SO$_4$ (98); Cl (252); free CO$_2$.	do	11 main springs. Small deposits of tufa, sulfur, alum. Water used for bathing and irrigation.
20	On Big Windy Creek, in canyon.	Hot	Moderately large			Granite intrusive	2 main and several smaller springs. Free H$_2$S.
21	On upper Flat Creek	Warm				Schist	
22	About 20 miles north of Glacier.	Warm				Gravel, probably overlying granite.	Supplies pool which does not freeze over in winter.
23	About 8 miles west of Glacier.	Warm				Quaternary gravel overlying gneiss.	Do.
24	On Otter Creek, 10 miles southeast of Iditarod.	Warm				Granite, at contact with slate.	Several springs; flow all winter. Iron oxide stains on rocks.
25	Near Tuluksak River, in Whitefish Lake area.	Hot				Probably granite intrusive in Cretaceous strata.	Several springs. Free H$_2$S.
26	Near head of Ophir Creek, in Whitefish Lake area.	150	Large			Granite intrusive in Carboniferous volcanic tuff.	Small amount of free H$_2$S. Water used for bathing. Large mound of siliceous sinter 13.5 miles farther southeast marks site of former thermal springs.
27	On Twelvemile Creek	Hot				Altered Paleozoic strata	Water rises in pools. Ref. 177.
28	Attu Island	Warm				Lava	Near solfataric volcano. Ref. 171.
29	Little Sitkin Island	Hot				do	Ref. 171.
30	Semisopochnoi (Semiseisopochnoi) Island.	Hot				do	Ref. 172.
31	At Hot Springs Bay on Tanaga Island.	Hot				do	
32	At base of volcano on Kánaga Island.	[3] 219				do	Hot springs and fumaroles. Water used for cooking food. Refs. 160, 166.
33	Near White volcano on Adak (Adakh) Island.	Hot				do	Refs. 155, 160, 166, 171.
34	Great Sitkin Island	190–208				do	12 main springs, also mud pots and fumaroles, at altitude of 2,000 ft. Refs. 153, 171, 173.
35	Near Conical volcano on Atka (Athka) Island.	Hot				do	Mud pools, some boiling. Water is sulfurous. Ref. 155.
36	Near Kliuchef volcano on Atka (Athka) Island.	Hot				do	Ref. 160.
37	About 5 miles from Koróvin Bay on Atka (Athka) Island.	167				do	Ref. 155.
38	Seguam Island	Hot				do	Springs and hot mud pools. Ref. 160.
39	At base of volcano on Chuginadak Island.	Hot				do	Ref. 160.
40	Kagamil Island	Hot				do	Springs and fumaroles. Ref. 160.

See footnotes at end of table.

No. on fig. 9	Name or location	Temperature of water (°F)	Flow (gpm)	Total dissolved solids (ppm)	Principal chemical constituents	Associated rocks	Remarks and additional references
41	Northeast of Vsevidof volcano on Umnak Island.	43–68	52,000	--------	--------	Lava	16 springs, including 1 geyser; also fumaroles. Water contains as much as 159 ppm of B_2O_3. Refs. 83, 153, 171.
42	Central part of Umnak Island.	214	--------	1,377	SiO_2 (150); Ca (39); Na (350); HCO_3 (29) SO_4 (130); Cl (483); B_2O_3 (157).	----do----	Small geyser.
43	Near Hot Springs Cove on Umnak Island.	95–215	--------	2,282	SiO_2 (88); Ca (164); Na (606); HCO_3 (67); SO_4 (88); Cl (1,133); B_2O_3 (92).	----do----	28 springs, including several small geysers. Analysis is for water having temperature of 192°F. Ref. 153.
44	Bogoslof and New Bogoslof Islands.	Hot	--------	--------	--------	----do----	Intermittent and steady jets of steam from many vents. Refs. 156, 157, 160, 169, 175, 177.
45	Makushin volcano on Unalaska (Unalashka, Oonalashka) Island.	94				----do----	Several springs. Solfataras in the crater. Refs. 155, 160, 166, 168, 171.
46	Akutan Island, including springs at head of Long Creek and in Hot Springs Bay valley.	[3]181		[1]952	SiO_2 (129); Ca (10); Na (288); HCO_3 (192); SO_4 (39); Cl (350); B_2O_3 (36).	Lava	Several springs and steam vents. Refs. 152, 155, 159, 171.
47	Islet northwest of Akutan Island.	Hot	--------			----do----	Ref. 160.
48	Islet southeast of Akutan Island.	Hot				----do----	Several springs issuing on beach between tide levels. Ref. 155.
49	Near Pogromni volcano on Unimak Island.	Hot				----do----	Many springs; also hot marshes. Refs. 160, 166.
50	Near Morzhovoi (Morshevoi) village.	Hot				----do----	Water is sulfurous. Refs. 160, 171.
51	Amagat Island, near Morzhovoi Bay.	Hot				----do----	Refs. 155, 160, 166.
52	Near Pavlov volcano	140	Large			----do----	Several main springs; also fumaroles on southwest slope of Mount Hague. Ref. 160.
53	Near Balboa Bay	Hot					
54	Port Moller	150–180				Recent lava overlying limestone.	1 main and several minor pools. Water tastes alkaline. Much free gas. Refs. 160, 166.
55	Near Port Heiden	Hot				Probably Cretaceous strata.	Water issues near shore.
56	Southwest shore of Becharof Lake near base of Mount Peulik.	--------				Jurassic sandstone probably intruded by lava.	
57	Near Katmai Pass	Hot	Large			Lava	Much free H_2S. Deposits of ocher and sulfur. Refs. 161, 174.
58	Near Mount Katmai, including those in Valley of Ten Thousand Smokes.	Hot				Lava and tuff	Several springs and many fumaroles. Refs. 119, 151, 158, 161, 163, 164, 182, 183.
59	West Fork of Douglas River, 25 miles west of Cape Douglas.	Hot	Large			Jurassic strata	
60	Near shore of Lituya Bay	Warm				Tertiary strata	
61	Near head of Mud Bay	Hot				Paleozoic strata	
62	Near Nika Bay	Hot				----do----	
63	North shore of Lisianski Inlet.	Hot				----do----	
64	4 miles above head of Tenakee Inlet.	81–179	10	[1]592	SiO_2 (119); Na (137); SO_4 (226); Cl (33); free H_2S.	Diorite intrusive in granite.	12 springs issuing near creek. Small deposits of tufa.
65	Hooniah, 75 yd from shore	84–111	30	[1]276	SiO_2 (96); Na + K (59); HCO_3 (18); CO_3 (25); Cl (42); small amount of free H_2S.	Schist	3 springs. Water used for bathing.
66	Near North Arm of Peril Strait.	101–103	3	[4]786	Na (206); SO_4 (329); Cl (133)	Fractured diorite	4 main springs issuing on shore between low and high tide levels.
67	Tenakee, on north shore of Tenakee Inlet.	56–106	22	[1]787	SiO_2 (94); Na (201); SO_4 (302); Cl (99); free CO_2, H_2S.	Granite intrusive in gneiss.	10 main springs. Bathing resort. Ref. 180.
68	3 miles east of head of Fish Bay.	62–117	25	[1]393	SiO_2 (110); Na + K (69); HCO_3 (43); CO_3 (63); B_4O_7 (34); small amount of free H_2S.	Faulted schist	24 springs issuing along bank of small creek. Water used for bathing.
69	Baranof	60–122	80	[1]268	SiO_2 (96); Na + K (58); HCO_3 (93); SO_4 (49).	Faulted granite and diorite.	9 springs. Bathhouses; cabins. Ref. 180.
70	Sitka, near shore 16 miles south of Sitka.	95–149	13	[1]4,877	SiO_2 (96); Ca (378); Na (1,440); SO_4 (88); Cl. (2,745); free H_2S.	Granite cut by diabase dikes.	3 main springs, 124°–149°F. Bathing resort. Ref. 166, 180.
71	Near north side of Gut Bay	Warm				Paleozoic limestone and schist.	Water is sulfurous.
72	North side of Stikine River, 18 miles northeast of Wrangell.	Hot	Small			Alluvium overlying intrusive granite.	
73	Shake's, 20 miles northeast of Wrangell.	[3]125	100	[1]409	SiO_2 (108); Na (87); HCO_3 (43); SO_4 (142).	Granite	Several springs. Bathhouse.
74	South side of Stikine River, 8 miles north of Wrangell.	Hot	Small			Probably Paleozoic strata, near granitic batholith.	
75	South end of Vank Island, 8 miles west of Wrangell.	Hot				----do----	Issues on beach between low and high tide levels.
76	Bailey Bay	145–191	83	413	SiO_2 (142); Na + K (54); HCO_3 (27); CO_3 (52); small amount of free H_2S.	Granite	9 main springs. Analysis is for water having temperature of 186°F. Water used for bathing. Ref. 180.
77	North bank of Unuk River	Warm	Small			----do----	Ref. 181.
78	5 miles southeast of Saks Cove.	150	10			----do----	
79	Bell Island	109–162	10	[1]674	SiO_2 (105); Na + K (201); SO_4 (129); Cl (188); small amount of free H_2S.	Granite cut by pegmatite dikes.	Temperature of water from 5 main springs ranges from 125° to 162°F. Bathhouse.

[1] Hottest.
[2] Main spring.
[3] Maximum.
[4] Coolest.

RATING CHART

What are the characteristics that make a hot spring desirable? That depends on what an individual is looking for. Are you cost-conscious? Love privacy? Like the amenities . . . a bathhouse, a nearby restaurant, lodging? It's obvious that a hot spring cannot be all things to all people. So instead of trying to recommend a particular hot spring, we've developed the following rating chart which will permit you to decide for yourself.

The items listed are not in any particular order of importance. Thus, we suggest that you supply information about those that you think are important. We'll include your comments and data in our next edition.   Thanks,   The Authors.

Location:

Temperature:

Flow rate:

Size:

Developed:

Undeveloped:

Conventional pool:

In natural form:

Far from any civilization:

Close to civilization:

Various amenities (lodging, foot, etc.):

Scenic beauty:

Privacy:

Protection from the elements:

Convenience of access:

Camping possibilities nearby:

Geological interest:

Big enough for a gang:

Small enough for two friendly people:

Available all year round or
    seasonal climate:

Drive in, walk in:

Fee to swim or free:

Can you control temperature:

Is there a series of pools of varying temp.:

Natural or man made shower:

Individual baths in addition to large pool:

Massage available:

Other health services:

Cold water:

Proximity of a stream, creek, river or
    ocean for contrasting bath:

Dangerous or threatening animals nearby (many
    hot springs are used also as cattle drinking
    troughs and some of these enclosures contain
    ferocious bulls:

Insect problems:

Beneficial minerals for bathing or drinking:

Ease of entry into water (sharp mineral deposits,
    mud or muck, slithery beasts, pier, ladder,
    stairway, handrail, slide, swing or rope diving
    board):

Can you wash car, dishes or laundry:

Water movement (Do you get a natural turbu-
    lence from a flowing hot stream or river, such
    as Hot Creek, CA., or bubbling up action):

Could it be developed:

Is it for sale, lease or rent:

Could it be used for other than bathing, i.e.,
    agriculture, water for animals, geothermal
    power, greenhouse, hydroponics, heating a
    house, keep roads clear of snow and ice:

A THANK YOU PAGE

First, to the Geological Survey people in Washington for providing the excellent maps and directory that appear herein. We hope to return the favor soon by sending in some new data and even news of a hot spring or two that wasn't listed.

Second, to the wonderful people along the way; hot spring visitors, resort owners, and casual acquaintances who helped us find, enjoy, and document the various springs. Special mention to the many friendly farmers who pointed weathered fingers towards outasite springs, some nearly forgotten by natives of the region.

Next, to publisher Noel Young whose enthusiasm for this project made it a reality. Noel shares our love of the waters of the earth, whether they be hot or cold, salt or fresh, wild or captured.

A tribute to Ruth, an intrepid adventurer who braved snakes slithering around Hot Pond in southeast Oregon and a gasoline shortage in northern Arizona to help put it all together.

And thanks to Wendy and Jill, my daughters who steered me towards my first hot spring adventure in the back country of Santa Barbara. They casually mentioned that some young friends had spent a weekend around Big Caliente enjoying fried chicken, French bread and the soothing 120 degree water that courses down the slopes into the family-sized pool.

Appreciation is also extended to those who responded to our queries concerning various springs, providing photos and data incorporated in this edition.

ISBN 0-912264-89-6 $4.95

Descriptions of great hot springs in California,
Oregon, Idaho, Nevada, and New Mexico,
with a full Directory of 1000 hot springs
in the western United States.

John Muir made two ascents of Mount Shasta. The
second, undertaken in late winter, nearly cost him
his life. A snowstorm forced him and his compan-
ion to seek refuge at a hot springs on the slopes of
Shasta. Although it was the type which vents live
steam and corrosive gases, it provided sufficient
heat to prevent Muir and his friend from freezing
to death. Here is a brief selection in Muir's own
words:

*"Jerome made a dash from the shelter of the lava-
block and began forcing his way back against the
wind to the hot springs, wavering and struggling
to resist being carried away, as if he were fording a
rapid stream. 'Here', said Jerome, 'we shall be safe
from frost.' 'Yes,' said I, 'we can lie in this mud
and steam and sludge—warm at least on one
side.' "*